Teacher Anthology 1

GENERAL EDITOR

JACK BOOTH

DAVID BOOTH

WILLA PAULI & JO PHENIX

I M P R E S S I O N S

HOLT, RINEHART AND WINSTON OF CANADA, LIMITED

Sponsoring Editor: Sheba Meland
Senior Editor: Wendy Cochran
Developmental Editor: Nancy McMeekan
Production Editor: Jocelyn Van Huyse
Art Director: Wycliffe Smith
Design Assistant: Julia Naimska
Cover: Joanne Fitzgerald

ISBN 0-03-921407-9

Canadian Cataloguing in Publication Data
Main entry under title:
Teacher anthology 1
(Impressions)
Supplement to grade 1 level readers in the Impressions series.
ISBN 0-03-921407-9

1. Reading (Primary) – Study and teaching. I. Booth,
Jack, 1946-   I. Series: Impressions (Toronto, Ont.).
LB1573.T32 1983   428.6   C83-009178-6

Acknowledgements

One, One, Cinnamon Bun: From CATCH ME & KISS ME & SAY IT AGAIN, text © 1978 by Clyde Watson. Reprinted by permission of Philomel Books, a Division of Putnam Publishing Group. *The New Teacher*: By Miriam Cohen. Reprinted with permission of Macmillan Publishing Company from THE NEW TEACHER by Miriam Cohen. Copyright © 1972 by Miriam Cohen. *Who's in Peter Rabbit's House?*: By Verna Aardema. Text copyright © 1969, 1977 by Verna Aardema. Reprinted by permission of Dial Books for Young Readers, A Division of E.P. Dutton, Inc. *The ABC Bunny*: By Wanda Gag, reprinted by permission of Coward-McCann. Copyright 1933 by Wanda Gag, copyright renewed © 1961 by Robert Janssen. *Rum, Pum, Pum*: A folk tale from India retold by Maggie Duff. Reprinted with permission of Macmillan Publishing Company from RUM, PUM, PUM — a folk tale from India retold by Maggie Duff. Copyright © 1978 by Maggie Duff. *Rattlesnake Skipping Song*: By Dennis Lee. From ALLIGATOR PIE by Dennis Lee. Reprinted by permission of Macmillan of Canada (A Division of Gage Publishing Limited). *The Seven Skinny Goats*: By Victor G. Ambrus. The text of THE SEVEN SKINNY GOATS by Victor G. Ambrus © Victor G. Ambrus 1969. By permission of Oxford University Press. *The Balloon*: By Karla Kuskin from IN THE MIDDLE OF THE TREES by Karla Kuskin. Copyright © 1958 by Karla Kuskin, reprinted by permission of the author. *Raccoon*: By William Jay Smith. From LAUGHING TIME by William Jay Smith. Copyright © 1953, 1955, 1956, 1957, 1959, 1968, 1974, 1977, 1980, by William Jay Smith. Reprinted by permission of Delecorte Press — Seymour Lawrence. A Merloyd Lawrence Book. *Here Come Raccoons!*: By Lillian Hoban. Copyright © 1977 by Lillian Hoban. Reprinted by permission of Holt, Rinehart and Winston, Publishers. *Ranzo*: From YOU CAN'T CATCH ME by Michael Rosen. Text copyright © 1981 by Michael Rosen. Reprinted by permission of the publishers, André Deutsch Ltd. *What's in Father's Sack?*: By Paul Galdone. Copyright © 1982 by Paul Galdone. Reprinted by permission of Ticknor & Fields/Clarion Books, a Houghton Mifflin Company. *Imagine*: By Roland Egan, from HAVE YOU HEARD THE SUN SINGING, edited by Adrian Rumble. Reprinted by permission of Bell & Hyman Limited. *Tikki Tikki Tembo*: Retold by Arlene Mosel. Copyright © 1968 by Arlene Mosel. Reprinted by permission of Holt, Rinehart and Winston, Publishers. *Some One*: By Walter de la Mare. Reprinted by permission of The Literary Trustees of Walter de la Mare and The Society of Authors as their representative. *Little Sister and the Month Brothers*: By Beatrice Schenk De Regniers. Text copyright © 1976 by Beatrice Schenk De Regniers. Reprinted by permission of Ticknor & Fields/Clarion Books, a Houghton Mifflin Company. *Us Two*: By A.A. Milne. From NOW WE ARE SIX by A.A. Milne, used by permission of The Canadian Publishers, McClelland and Stewart Limited, Toronto. *How Rabbit Stole the Fire*: By Joanna Troughton. Reproduced by kind permission of The Blackie Publishing Group, Scotland. *Hildilid's Night*: By Cheli Duran Ryan. Reprinted with permission of Macmillan Publishing Company from HILDILID'S NIGHT by Cheli Duran Ryan. Copyright © 1971 by Cheli Duran Ryan. *Snow*: By Karla Kuskin from DOGS & DRAGONS, TREES & DREAMS: A Collection of Poems by Karla Kuskin. Copyright © 1968 by Karla Kuskin. By permission of Harper & Row, Publishers, Inc. *The Lad Who Went to the North Wind*: From THE OLD WOMAN AND HER PIG and 10 Other Stories written and illustrated by Anne Rockwell. Copyright © 1979 by Anne Rockwell. A Thomas Y. Crowell book. By permission of Harper & Row, Publishers, Inc. *The Monkeys and the Crocodile*: From TIRRA LIRRA by Laura E. Richards. Published by Little, Brown and Company. *All the Way Home*: By Lore Segal. Reprinted by permission of Farrar, Straus and Giroux, Inc. ALL THE WAY HOME, story by Lore Segal, pictures by James Marshall. Text copyright © 1973 by Lore Segal, pictures copyright © 1973 by James Marshall. *Bedtime*: From ELEANOR FARJEON'S POEMS FOR CHILDREN (J.B. Lippincott Co.). Copyright 1933, 1961 by Eleanor Farjeon. By permission of Harper & Row, Publishers, Inc. *How the Little Old Woman Kept Her Geese Warm*: By Hope Newell. From THE LITTLE OLD WOMAN WHO USED HER HEAD by Hope Newell. Copyright, 1935, by Thomas Nelson and Sons; renewal, 1963, by Hope Newell. Reprinted by permission of E.P. Dutton, Inc. *Conversation*: By Rose Fyleman. Reprinted by permission of The Society of Authors as the literary representative of the Estate of Rose Fyleman. *Big Sister and Little Sister*: Text only of BIG SISTER AND LITTLE SISTER by Charlotte Zolotow. Copyright © 1966 by Charlotte Zolotow. Reprinted by permission of Harper & Row, Publishers, Inc. *Me and My Giant*: In WHERE THE SIDEWALK ENDS; The Poems and Drawings of Shel Silverstein. Copyright © 1974 by Shel Silverstein. By permission of Harper & Row, Publishers, Inc. *Puppy and I*: By A.A. Milne. From WHEN WE WERE VERY YOUNG by A.A. Milne. Used by permission of The Canadian Publishers, McClelland and Stewart Limited, Toronto. *Mrs. Beggs and the Wizard*: By Mercer Mayer. Reprinted by permission of Four Winds Press, a division of Scholastic Inc. from MRS. BEGGS AND THE WIZARD by Mercer Mayer. Copyright © 1973 by Mercer Mayer. *Beware of Me!*: By Norman H. Russell. Copyright Norman H. Russell, 1968. Reprinted by permission of the author. *The Three Billy Goats Gruff*: From POPULAR TALES FROM THE NORSE by Peter Christian Asbjörnsen & Jörgen Moe. Reprinted by permission of G.P. Putnam's Sons. *Open the Door*: By Marion Edey is reprinted with the permission of Charles Scribner's Sons from OPEN THE DOOR: RHYMES FOR CHILDREN. Copyright 1949 by Marion Edey and Dorothy Grider. *Half-a-Ball-of-Kenki*: Adapted from AKAN-ASHANTI FOLK-TALES by R.S. Rattray (1930). By permission of Oxford University Press. *The Mysterious Cat*: By Vachel Lindsay. Reprinted with permission of Macmillan Publishing Company from COLLECTED POEMS by Vachel Lindsay. Copyright 1914 by Macmillan Publishing Co., Inc., renewed 1942 by Elizabeth C. Lindsay. *The Bunyip of Berkeley's Creek*: By Jenny Wagner (Longman Young Books/Childerset 1973). Copyright © 1973 by Ron Brooks and Childerset Pty. Ltd. Reprinted by permission of Penguin Books Ltd. *Good Morning*: By Mark Van Doren. Reprinted by permission of Hill & Wang, now a division of Farrar, Straus and Giroux, Inc. "Good Morning" from GOOD MORNING by Mark Van Doren. Copyright © 1972, 1973 by the Estate of Mark Van Doren. *The King's Monster*: By Carolyn Haywood. Copyright © 1980 by Carolyn Haywood. By permission of William Morrow & Company. *Did You Feed My Cow?*: (first two stanzas) from GOLDEN SLIPPERS, edited by Arna Bontemps. Copyright 1941 by Harper & Row, Publishers, Inc. By permission of Harper & Row, Publishers, Inc. *The Greyling*: By Jane Yolen. Reprinted by permission of Philomel Books, a Division of The Putnam Publishing Group, from THE GREYLING by Jane Yolen. Copyright © 1968 by Jane Yolen. *Little Cat*: By Laura E. Richards from I HAVE A SONG TO SING YOU by Laura E. Richards, copyright 1938, D. Appleton-Century Co., Inc. *The Girl Who Loved the Wind*: By Jane Yolen (Thomas Y. Crowell Co.). Copyright 1972 by Berne Convention. ALL RIGHTS RESERVED. By permission of Harper & Row, Publishers, Inc. *A Baby Sister for Frances*: By Russell Hoban. Text copyright © 1964 by Russell Hoban. By permission of Harper & Row, Publishers, Inc. *The Three Sillies*: From THE OLD WOMAN AND HER PIG and 10 Other Stories written and illustrated by Anne Rockwell. Copyright © 1979 by Anne Rockwell. A Thomas Y. Crowell book. By permission of Harper & Row, Publishers, Inc. *Oodles of Noodles*: By Lucia and James L. Hymes, Jr. Text © MCMLXIV by Lucia M. and James L. Hymes, Jr. Published by Addison-Wesley, Reading, Massachusetts, A Young Scott Book. Reprinted with permission of the publisher. *The Terrible Nung Gwama*: Adapted by Ed Young from the retelling by Leslie Bonnet, © 1978 by Leslie Bonnet; © 1978 by Ed Young. Reprinted by permission of Philomel Books, a Division of Putnam Publishing Group. *The Tutti Frutti Tree*: By Monica Hughes. Printed with permission of the author, MONICA HUGHES © 1983. *When the Drum Sang*: By Anne Rockwell. Reprinted by permission of Curtis Brown, Ltd. Copyright © 1970 by Anne Rockwell. *Let's Send a Rocket*: By Kit Patrickson from POEMS FOR ME by Kit Patrickson. Reprinted by permission of Ginn and Company Ltd., Aylesbury, England. *How the Rooster Saved the Day*: By Arnold Lobel. Copyright © 1977 by Arnold Lobel. By permission of Greenwillow Books (A Division of William Morrow & Company). *What's in There?*: From HERE WE COME A'PIPING. Reprinted by permission of Granger Book, Co. *Why Mosquitoes Buzz in People's Ears*: By Verna Aardema. Text copyright © 1975 by Verna Aardema. Reprinted by permission of Dial Books for Young Readers, A Division of E.P. Dutton, Inc. *Ferry Boats*: From CRICKETY CRICKET! The Best Loved Poems by James Tippett. Copyright 1929 by Harper & Row, Publishers, Inc. *Apt. 3*: By Ezra Jack Keats. Reprinted with permission of Macmillan Publishing Company from APT. 3 by Ezra Jack Keats. Copyright © 1971 by Ezra Jack Keats. *My Big Blue Boat*: From PLAYTIME TUNES FOR THE NURSERY SCHOOL by Marion Anderson; © J.B. CRAMER & CO., LTD., 99 St. Martin's Lane, London, WC2N 4AZ. Reproduced by permission. *Mud Puddle*: By Robert Munsch, published by Annick Press Ltd., Toronto © Rober Munsch 1979. Reprinted by permission of the publishers. *I'm Tipingee, She's Tipingee, We're Tipingee, Too*: From THE MAGIC ORANGE TREE AND OTHER HAITIAN FOLKTALES, by Diane Wolkstein. Copyright © 1978 by Diane Wolkstein. Reprinted by permission of Alfred A. Knopf, Inc.

Printed in Canada   1 2 3 4 5   87 86 85 84 83

Table of Contents

Teacher Anthology 1

INTRODUCTION

Research indicates a strong connection between a child's success in reading and his or her awareness of stories, poems, and knowledge of the purpose of books. Reading aloud to children promotes a love of literature, develops an awareness of and appreciation for a variety of literary structures, patterns, and styles, and builds an understanding of narrative.

The *Teacher Anthology* contains selections that are intended to be read aloud by the teacher. In this way, the children are exposed to quality literature that they are not able to read on their own. The selections correspond to the units in the IMPRESSIONS Readers. They include nursery rhymes, folk and fairy tales, legends, contemporary stories, and poems. It is important to know the selection well before it is read to the children. You, the teacher, can decide what mood to set, what tone to use, what voices to enact, and whether to read the entire story at one time.

Various activities and strategies are included in the teacher notes that accompany each selection in the *Teacher Anthology*. The stories and poems should be read in correspondence to the reader selections. The selections are intended to be companion pieces so that a child's vocabulary and concept development are not limited by his or her reading ability.

Language learning is an integrated process: listening to literature opens the children to experiences, to new and different language patterns, to exciting images that enlarge their backgrounds, thus allowing them to bring meaning to the printed page. This anthology will help you, the teacher, broaden the children's print/listening experience and assist each child in his or her endeavor to learn to read, making it a more holistic experience.

As the teacher reads, the children can create the pictures in their minds and imaginations about the stories and poems. Then, these can be shared in discussion, art, and writing so that the literature will be a stimulus for shared learning.

One, One, Cinnamon Bun

This is a poem for chanting aloud. Read the
poem to the class rhythmically and joyfully
twice, then have the children say the first
line of each verse (the number repeated
twice) while you complete the stanza.
Children may wish to clap along quietly
with the rhythm. Divide the lines among
the children so that the whole class says the
first line of each stanza, and a group or an
individual says the second line.

      class: One, one
      pupil: Cinnamon bun
      class: Two, two
      two pupils: Chicken stew
      . . . and so on.

One, one
Cinnamon bun

Two, two
Chicken stew

Three, three
Cakes and tea

Four, four
I want more

Five, five
Honey in a hive

Six, six
Pretzel sticks

Seven, seven
Straight from heaven

Eight, eight
Clean your plate

Nine, nine
Look at mine

Ten, ten
Start over again!

TRADITIONAL

2

The New Teacher

By Miriam Cohen

Before the story

Ask the children for stories they have heard
about school from their friends and families.
Do their parents have stories about when
they were children in school? What
information do the children have about
school (location, size, etc.)?

After the story

Discuss why the children were so worried
about the teacher. Ask what the parents
could have done to make the children feel
better. What things have they been nervous
about that turned out fine?

The teacher went away to have a baby.
Everybody in first grade loved her. They
didn't see why she needed a baby when
she had the whole first grade.

Today there was going to be a new teacher.
Jim looked for Paul in the playground. Paul was
his best friend.

Paul wasn't there, but Willy and Sammy
were. They were pushing each other into the
trash cans.

"Hey, Jim!" said Willy.

"We saw the new teacher. She's a big lady!"

And Sammy said, "A big lady can holler
loud."

Paul came running. He was in a hurry to tell
a riddle. "What is white, has one horn, and
gives milk?"

Jim didn't know.

"The answer is—a milk truck!" Paul said.

They all laughed. It was a good riddle.

Jim wanted to make everybody laugh. "What
is big, very big," he said, "and hollers loud,
like a cow?"

"I don't know," Paul said.

"The new teacher!" shouted Jim.

Paul and Willy and Sammy and Jim laughed
a lot.

Danny was chasing the girls and making them
scream. The girls didn't like Danny but they
did like to scream.

Paul called, "Danny! Listen to Jim's riddle!"

Danny laughed. "That's funny, Jim!"

Jim felt good when Danny said that.

Jim looked over the playground. He was
looking for somebody else to tell his riddle to.

Everybody was whirling and jumping,
pushing and laughing. In a corner, George was
hiding the hardboiled egg from his lunch.

He looked in the lunch bag to see if his
cupcake was still there. To be sure it was safe,
he ate it.

Anna-Maria and Margaret were jumping rope
very fast.

"I had a little hot dog
I kept him in a bun
I told my little hot dog
Run, run, run!
Picalilly, chili
Kitchup, ketchup
Red hot pepper!"

Jim ran to tell them his riddle about the new
teacher.

"Did you make it up?" asked Anna-Maria.

Jim nodded.

"It's not very good," said Anna-Maria.

Paul and Danny galloped up. "Say more funny

things about the new teacher, Jim!"

"Well," said Jim, "she huffs herself up bigger and bigger, and smoke comes out of her mean, green nose."

"Mean, green nose! Ha! Ha!" shouted Danny.

"Then," said Jim, "then she screams and hollers, '*Read!* Don't you know how to read?' "

"That's not funny," Danny said. He couldn't read.

It didn't really seem funny to Jim. He couldn't read either. Anna-Maria was the only one in first grade who could.

First grade was getting in line. But not Danny. Danny began to walk big and heavy and scary like Frankenstein. *"I'm the-new-teacher!"* he said.

Jim wished Danny would stop. He wished he hadn't thought of the new teacher with smoke coming out of her mean, green nose.

Paul always saved Jim's place next to him. They held hands very tight. Then they went into the first grade room.

There she was—the new teacher. She was big! She did holler!

She hollered, "Hi, everybody. I'm glad to see you. I think we're going to have a good time together!"

And before the morning was over, Jim and the whole first grade thought so too.

Here Comes a Big Red Bus

This poem can be the basis for a movement lesson. Read the poem to the class once or twice and have them join in when they are able. (You can give the last line each time if the children have difficulty remembering it.) The children can move about the room as if they were driving the vehicle—slowly for the big bus and quickly for the automobile. Use a hand clap or a tambourine to freeze or control their actions. They may wish to suggest other vehicles from the story "The Highway" in *How I Wonder*.

Here comes a big red bus, -
A big red bus, a big red bus;
Here comes a big red bus,
To take us to the stores

Here comes a mini bus, etc.
To take us all to school.

Here comes an automobile, etc.
To take us on a trip.

TRADITIONAL

Who's in Rabbit's House?

RETOLD BY VERNA AARDEMA

Before the story

Ask the children for their choice of the quietest animal, of the most frightening animal, of the largest animal, of the smallest animal, of the animal that scares other animals.

After the story

Ask the children, "Which animal saved Rabbit's home for him? What animals can you remember from the story? Can you remember the sequence of the animals in the story? Why do you think the caterpillar was in the house in the first place?"

Long, long ago a rabbit lived on a bluff overlooking a lake. A path went by her door and down the bank to the water. The animals of the forest used that path when they went to the lake to drink.

Every day, at dusk, Rabbit sat in her doorway and watched them.

But one evening she came to her house and she could not get in.

And a big, bad voice from inside the house roared, "I am The Long One. I eat trees and trample on elephants. Go away! Or I will trample on you!"

"That's my house!" cried Rabbit. "Come out at once!" She banged on the door, *ban, ban, ban!*

But the bad animal said more crossly than before, "Go away! Or I will trample on you!" And the rabbit sat down on a nearby log to think.

Now a frog happened to see this. She hopped up to the rabbit and said rather timidly, "I think I could get him out." *"Nuh!"* sniffed the rabbit. "You are so small. You think you could do what I cannot? You annoy me! Go away!"

Frog would have left that rude rabbit if a jackal had not come along just then.

Instead she crouched—*semm*—behind a nearby tree to see what would happen.

The jackal said, "Ho, Rabbit, why aren't you sitting in your doorway?"

"Someone's in my house," said the rabbit. "He won't come out. And I can't get in."

Jackal looked at the little house. "Who's in Rabbit's house?" he asked.

The bad voice replied, "I am The Long One. I eat trees and trample on elephants. Go away! Or I will trample on you!"

"I'm going!" cried Jackal. And off he went— *kpidu, kpidu, kpidu.*

The frog laughed softly to herself.

The jackal came back. He said, "I think I know what to do. We must gather a big pile of sticks."

They did.

"Now," said Jackal, "we'll put the sticks close to the house. Like this." And *kabak*, he pushed the whole pile of sticks against the door.

"But, Jackal," protested the rabbit, "that will keep him in! Not get him out!"

At that the frog nearly burst with mirth.

Jackal said, "I'm going to set fire to the sticks."

"Fire!" cried the rabbit. "That would burn my house!"

"It would burn The Long One too!" said Jackal.

"I won't let you burn my house!" cried Rabbit. "Go away!"

So the jackal trotted off *kpata, kpata* down to the lake.

Rabbit began to pick up the sticks. A leopard came by. "What are you doing, Rabbit?" he asked. "Are you putting sticks there to hide your house?"

"No, not that!" cried the rabbit. "Someone's in my house. Jackal wanted to burn him out. Now I have to take this wood away."

Leopard watched as Rabbit removed the sticks. Then he asked, "Who's in Rabbit's house?"

The bad voice said, "I am The Long One. I eat trees and trample on elephants. Go away! Or I will trample on you!"

"*Nn-huu!*" snorted the leopard. "You don't scare me! I'm tough! I'll tear that house to bits and eat you up!" And he leaped on top of the little house and began to scratch, scratch, scratch. Bits of the roof went flying—*zzt, zzt, zzt.* "Stop!" cried the rabbit. "Don't spoil my house!"

"How can you use it—with a bad animal in it?" asked Leopard.

"But it's still my house!" said Rabbit. "Go away!"

So the leopard jumped down. And *pa, pa, pa* he went down to the lake.

And the frog grinned and chuckled to herself.

Rabbit climbed onto her roof. She smoothed and patted it—*bet, bet, bet!*

An elephant came by. "What happened, Rabbit?" she asked. "Does your roof leak?"

"No, not that!" cried the rabbit. "Someone's in my house. Leopard wanted to tear it to bits and eat him. So I had to fix my roof." She gave the roof another pat and hopped down.

"Who's in Rabbit's house?" demanded the elephant.

The bad voice said, "I am The Long One. I eat trees and trample on elephants. Go away! Or I will trample on you!"

"Trample on elephants?" sneered the elephant. "Who thinks he tramples on elephants! I'll trample you flat! Flat as a mat! I'll trample you—house and all!"

Gumm, gumm, gumm went Elephant toward the little house.

Rabbit leaped in front of her. "Don't smash my house!" she screamed.

"I'm only trying to help," said the elephant.

Rabbit said, "I don't want that kind of help.

Go away!"

So the elephant tramped off *gumm, gumm, gumm* down to the lake.

And the frog laughed aloud—*gdung, gdung, gdung.*

"Stop laughing, Frog," said the rabbit. "See what that stupid elephant did to my yard. Now I have to smooth it." She found her hoe and set to work. *Kok, kok,* went the hoe.

A rhinoceros came by. He asked, "What are you doing, Rabbit? Are you making a farm here by your house?"

Rabbit stamped her foot. "No, not that!" she cried. "Someone's in my house. Elephant wanted to trample him. She made holes in my yard!"

"Who's in Rabbit's house?" asked the rhinoceros.

The bad voice said, "I am The Long One. I eat trees and trample on elephants. Go away! Or I will trample on you!"

"*Fuuuu!*" fumed the rhinoceros. "I'll hook you on my horn and hoist you into the lake—house and all!" He put his head down and *ras, ras, ras* he went toward the little house. But the rabbit leaped onto his nose. She held his big horn with her little paws.

Rhinoceros tossed his head. Up and away went Rabbit—*WEO* over the lake! Then—*NGISH!*

The rhinoceros shook himself in a satisfied way. "That's the end of The Long One," he said.

"But that was *Rabbit* you threw into the lake!" protested Frog.

Rhinoceros looked. The little house was not gone. But the rabbit was. The two rushed *pamdal* down the bluff to save Rabbit.

Now when the rabbit hit the water, she went *dilak, dilak, dilak* to the bottom of the lake. She kicked, and up she popped to the surface.

Elephant was still drinking at the lake. She saw the rabbit come up. "Keep kicking!" she called. She swam out and put her trunk around the rabbit and carried her to shore. "I saved you," she said. "But I don't know why. You are nothing but a bother!"

"Thank you, Elephant," said Rabbit. Then she went up the hill to her house. But she still could not get in. She sat on the log and began to cry—*wolu, wolu, wolu.*

The frog came up from the lake. "Don't cry, Rabbit," she said. "I think I could get that bad animal out of your house—if you would let me try."

"How?" asked the rabbit.

Frog whispered, "Scare him out."

Rabbit whispered back, "But how?"

"Watch me," said the frog. She took a big leaf and curled it around to make a horn. When she talked into it, it made her voice very loud. She said through the horn, "WHO'S IN RABBIT'S HOUSE?"

The bad voice said, "I am The Long One. I eat trees and trample on elephants. Go away! Or I will trample on you!"

Frog said, "I am the spitting cobra! I can blind you with my poison! Now come out of that house, or I'll squeeze under the door and spit poison *ssih* into your eyes!"

Then *hirrrr* the door opened.

Out came a long green caterpillar. He was so scared, his legs were jumping *vityo, vityo,* *vityo*. He was looking everywhere—*rim, rim, rim*. "Where's the spitting cobra?" he cried. "Don't let the spitting cobra get me! I was only playing a joke!"

"It's only a caterpillar!" cried Rabbit.

"Only a caterpillar," echoed Frog. She called the other animals. How they laughed when they saw that the bad animal was only a caterpillar.

And Rabbit said, "Oh, Long One, the spitting cobra was only Frog!"

Then Frog laughed even harder. All one could see of her was her enormous laugh.

Then the big animals went away.

The Long One crawled up a tree.

Rabbit sat in her doorway.

And the frog sat on the log croaking with laughter—*gdung, gdung, gdung.*

The ABC Bunny

This is a "join in" poem. The children can
add the rhyming words, once they have
heard you read it aloud.

      For example:
      A for Apple, big and red.
      B for Bunny, snug a- _____

A for Apple, big and red
B for Bunny snug a-bed
C for Crash!
D for Dash!
E for Elsewhere in a flash
F for Frog—he's fat and funny
"Looks like rain," says he to Bunny
G for Gale!
H for Hail!
Hippy-hop goes Bunny's tail
I for Insects here and there
J for Jay with jaunty air
K for Kitten, catnip-crazy
L for Lizard—look how lazy
M for Mealtime—munch, munch, munch!
M-m-m these greens are good for lunch
N for Napping in a Nook
O for Owl with bookish look
P for prickly Porcupine
Pins and needles on his spine
Q for Quail
R for Rail
S for Squirrel Swishy-tail
T for Tripping back to Town
U for Up and Up-side-down
V for View
Valley too
W—"We welcome you!"
X for eXit—off, away
That's enough for us today
Y for You, take one last look
Z for Zero—close the book!

    WANDA GAG

Rum Pum Pum

Retold By Maggie Duff

Before the story

Discuss with the class various pets that the children have. Ask, "Why shouldn't wild creatures and birds be kept in cages as pets?"

During the story

Have the class join in with you on the reading of the lines *rum pum pum, rum pum pum, rum pum pum pum pum.*

After the story

Ask the children to recall the characters that helped Blackbird get his wife back. Help them to sequence their arrival by discussing what each one did to assist Blackbird.

Long ago in India a blackbird lived with his mate in a tree. Blackbird sang very sweetly.

One day the King heard him as he was passing by.

"Bring me that sweet-singing blackbird," said the King. "I will keep him in a cage in my palace."

So the King's men set out to capture Blackbird; but they caught his wife by mistake, for they looked exactly alike and the King's men couldn't tell the difference.

When Blackbird discovered his wife had been stolen, he was very angry. He decided to get her back by whatever means.

Blackbird tied a long, sharp thorn around his waist for a sword.

He took the skin of a dead frog to use as a shield.

On his head he put half a walnut shell for a helmet, and made the other half into a kettledrum by stretching a piece of skin across it.

Then he declared war on the King. Down the road he marched, beating his drum, *rum pum pum, rum pum pum, rum pum pum pum pum.*

Before long he met a cat.

"Where to?" asked Cat.

"To make war on the King. He stole my wife."

"I'll join you. The King drowned my kittens."

"Jump into my ear then," said Blackbird.

So Cat jumped into Blackbird's ear, curled up and went to sleep.

Blackbird marched on, beating his drum as he went, *rum pum pum, rum pum pum, rum pum pum pum pum.* Soon he met some ants.

"Where to?" asked the ants.

"To make war on the King. He stole my wife."

"We'll join you. The King poured boiling water into our hill."

"Crawl into my ear then," said Blackbird. The ants did.

Blackbird marched on down the road beating his drum, *rum pum pum, rum pum pum, rum pum pum pum pum,* until he met a stick.

"Where to?" asked Stick.

"To make war on the King. He stole my wife."

"I'll join you. The King tore me from my tree in a fit of temper."

"Get into my ear then," said Blackbird. So Stick did.

Not far from the King's palace Blackbird had to cross a river.

"Where to?" asked River.

"To make war on the King. He stole my wife."

"Then I will join you. The King has let my waters become polluted."

"Flow into my ear," said Blackbird.

As you can well imagine, Blackbird's ear was really full by now, but somehow River found a place.

Then, *rum pum pum, rum pum pum, rum pum pum pum pum,* Blackbird marched right up to the palace gates.

Thump thump thump, he knocked at the door.

"Who's there?" called out the gatekeeper.

"General Blackbird here," answered Blackbird, "come to make war on the King and get back his wife."

The gatekeeper looked out. When he saw Blackbird standing there with his thorn sword, frog-skin shield, helmet made from half a walnut shell, and carrying a kettledrum made from the other half, he laughed so hard he nearly fell off his stool. He had never in all his life seen anything so funny!

But after that he opened the gate and took Blackbird into the King's presence.

"What do you want?" demanded the King.

"I want my wife," said Blackbird.

"Well, you shan't have her," the King answered crossly.

"Then you will have to take the consequences," said Blackbird.

And with that he marched around the room beating his kettledrum, *rum pum pum, rum pum pum, rum pum pum pum pum.*

"Seize that insolent fellow and throw him into the henhouse tonight!" shouted the King. "Those hens will make short work of him."

So the King's men seized Blackbird.

That night when they threw him into the henhouse, the hens were already asleep. When all was quiet and everyone asleep in the palace, Blackbird sang out softly.

> "Come out, Catkin, come out of my ear,
> There are hens a-plenty here.
> Chase them till their feathers fly,
> Claw them as they flutter by."

So out came Cat to chase the hens. Such a squawking and running about! When they had all fluttered through the door and were out of sight, Cat jumped back into Blackbird's ear and went to sleep.

Next morning the King sent for a report. When he heard that the hens were all gone and Blackbird was marching around the henhouse beating on his drum, *rum pum pum, rum pum pum, rum pum pum pum pum,* he was very angry indeed.

"Take that impudent bird tonight and throw him into the stables where the wild horses are," shouted the King. "They'll soon finish him off."

So that night the King's men threw Blackbird in with the wild horses, but he flew up to the rafters before they could touch him. When all was quiet and everyone asleep in the palace, Blackbird sang out softly,

> "Come out of my ear and help me, Stick.
> Beat the horses to make them kick.
> Beat them till at dawn of day

They break the door and run away."
Out came Stick and did just that. Then back into Blackbird's ear Stick went.

When it was morning, the King sent for Blackbird's remains. Instead of remains, the King's men found the horses gone and Blackbird marching around the stables beating his drum, *rum pum pum, rum pum pum, rum pum pum pum pum.*

The King was furious. The horses had cost a lot of money.

"Throw that fellow into the elephants' pen tonight," shouted the King. "That will be the end of him."

So that night Blackbird was put into the elephants' pen. But before the sleepy elephants could waken to trample him, Blackbird found a safe place to hide. When all was quiet and everyone asleep in the palace, Blackbird sang out softly,

> "Come out of my ear and help me, ants.
> Crawl up the trunks of the elephants.
> Sting them, bite them on the head,
> Bite them till they fall down dead."

Out crawled the ants, right up the trunks of the elephants. They stung and bit the elephants on the head until they went quite mad and trampled each other. When they all lay dead, the ants crawled back into Blackbird's ear.

In the morning the King himself went to collect Blackbird's carcass. When he found the elephants all dead and Blackbird marching around beating his kettledrum, *rum pum pum, rum pum pum, rum pum pum pum pum,* the King was not only furious, he was desperate!

"I don't know how that fellow does it," he said, "but I must find out. Tonight tie him to my bedpost, and then we will see what we will see."

So that night Blackbird was tied to the King's bedpost. When all was quiet and everyone asleep in the palace (except the King, who only pretended to be), Blackbird sang out softly,

> "Come out, River, come out of my ear,
> Swirl around the bedroom here.
> Flood the room and float the bed,
> Flow right over the King's head."

Out came River, pour-pour-pouring. All around the room River flowed until the King's bed floated. When the King began to get wet, he sat up and shouted, "For heaven's sake, General Blackbird, take your wife and get out of here!"

So Blackbird found his wife and took her home.

They have lived happily in their tree ever since.

Rattlesnake Skipping Song

This Dennis Lee poem has all the rhythmic
qualities of the traditional nursery rhyme.
Read it aloud, and then have the children
join in. You can say a line and they can
repeat it. To keep the rhythm, children can
clap along with the poem.

Mississauga rattlesnakes
Eat brown bread.
Mississauga rattlesnakes
Fall down dead.
If you catch a caterpillar
Feed him apple juice;
But if you catch a rattlesnake
Turn him loose!

DENNIS LEE

The Seven Skinny Goats

BY VICTOR G. AMBRUS

Before the story

Play a movement game with the class in the gym. Use a lively record and have the children move to the rhythm, not moving their feet but just using their hands, then their torso, and finally their feet, in free movement. They can choose to be different animals and move accordingly, e.g. kangaroos, hippos, snakes, etc.

After the story

Ask the children, "Why do you think everyone joined in dancing when Jano played his flute? What do you think happened to Jano in the next village? Have you heard other stories about shepherds?"

The children can paint pictures of the seven skinny goats dancing to Jano's flute.

The Innkeeper was the happiest man in his town. He owned seven fine, fat goats and he was very, very proud of them.

One morning a boy called Jano passed by. He was a simple lad, with nothing in his pockets but his flute, which he played for his living. Sometimes, when he was hungry, he did other jobs as well.

He asked the Innkeeper if he could mind his goats for a lump of cheese and an onion a day; and the Innkeeper agreed.

Jano took the goats to the meadow, sat down, and ate his cheese and onion. Then he took out his flute.

As soon as he started to play, the goats began to dance. They were so busy dancing they did not eat a single blade of grass.

By the time they returned home, the goats looked a sorry sight. The Innkeeper stared at them in astonishment and demanded to know what had happened. Jano explained that he had only taken them to the meadow and had even played them a tune to keep them happy.

The Innkeeper was very angry and decided to find out for himself what was happening to his goats.

So next morning, he got up early.

When Jano set out with the goats, the Innkeeper followed secretly, and waited behind a bush to see what happened.

Jano sat down and ate his cheese and onion. Then he began to play a tune. The goats immediately stood up on their hindlegs and started to dance.

Before the Innkeeper could get over his surprise, he kicked left, kicked right, and in a moment had joined the goats in their dance.

The eight of them romped around the meadow and Jano, who thought they were enjoying themselves, went on playing with all his might.

When Jano finally stopped playing, the Innkeeper, all out of breath, pounced on him and rushed him straight to the Judge.

There, he told how under Jano's care his seven fat goats had become the seven skinniest goats in town, and demanded that Jano should be punished.

13

The Judge looked at the goats and certainly they were the skinniest goats he had ever seen. So he sentenced Jano to be put in a barrel by the Executioner and rolled down the steepest hill out of the town.

When the townsfolk heard of this, they came flocking to the hill.

After they put Jano in the barrel, the Judge asked him, kindly: "Well, my boy, have you any last wishes?" "Just to play one tune on my flute, please, your Honour," said Jano.

"Very well," agreed the Judge.

But the Innkeeper shouted in a panic: "Don't let him play again, whatever you do! Or at least tie me to a tree, first."

But nobody took any notice of him, and Jano began to play. All the people leapt about and started dancing in earnest.

The Innkeeper kicked right, kicked left, and shouted in despair: "I knew this would happen. I knew this would happen."

And the people shouted back at him: "If you knew it, why didn't you say so!" *Hop, hop.* "If you knew it, why didn't you say so!" *Hop, hop.*

Jano thought they were enjoying themselves since they kept on dancing, so he went on playing until at last they all fell to the ground, exhausted.

Then the Judge pulled himself together, and gasped:

"Get out of here, young man, and never, never come back again."

Jano could see that the Judge was angry, although he had danced as hard as anyone. So he took to his heels and ran. He thought the people of this town were very odd indeed, and he was glad not to be rolled out of town in a barrel.

"No matter how hungry I am," he vowed, "I will never again go into a town where they don't appreciate good music."

The Balloon

The class can discuss the fun of balloons—
their colours and shapes, balloons they have
owned, and occasions when they see
balloons.

   After reading the poem, the children can
decide if they would take a balloon trip
by hanging on to one and flying above the
trees, the leaves, and even the clouds,
or if they would prefer to remain on the
ground. You can then reread the poem,
ending with the lovely last two lines.

I went to the park
And I bought a balloon.
It sailed through the sky
Like a large orange moon.
It bumped and it fluttered
And swam with the clouds.
Small birds flew around it
In high chirping clouds.
It bounced and it balanced
And bowed with the breeze.
It skimmed past the leaves
On the tops of the trees.
And then as the day
Started turning to night
I gave a short jump
And I held the string tight
And home we all sailed
Through the darkening sky,
The orange balloon, the small birds
And I.

KARLA KUSKIN

The Elves and the Shoemaker

By The Brothers Grimm

Before the story

Ask the children, "Have you ever wished for a magic person, such as a fairy god-mother, to help you out of trouble? In what situations?"

After the story

With the class, make a list of all the fantasy characters they have heard of in stories or films, e.g. elves, fairies, R2 D2.

Through role-playing, have the children, as elves, discuss their next "help out" adventure; through mime, have them enact the invented scene.

There was once a shoemaker who worked very hard and was very honest; but still he could not earn enough to live upon, and at last all he had in the world was gone, except just leather enough to make one pair of shoes.

Then he cut them all ready to make up the next day, meaning to get up early in the morning to work. His conscience was clear and his heart light amidst all his troubles; so he went peaceably to bed, left all his cares to heaven, and fell asleep.

In the morning, after he had said his prayers, he set himself down to his work, when to his great wonder, there stood the shoes, all ready made, upon the table. The good man knew not what to say or think of this strange event. He looked at the workmanship; there was not one false stitch in the whole job, and all was so neat and true that it was a complete masterpiece.

That same day a customer came in, and the shoes pleased him so well that he willingly paid a price higher than usual for them; and the poor shoemaker with the money bought leather enough to make two pairs more. In the evening he cut out the work, and went to bed early that he might get up and begin betimes next

day. But he was saved all the trouble, for when he got up in the morning the work was finished ready to his hand.

Presently in came buyers, who paid him handsomely for his goods, so that he bought leather enough for four pairs more. He cut out the work again over night, and found it finished in the morning as before; and so it went on for some time; what was got ready in the evening was always done by daybreak, and the good man soon became thriving and prosperous again.

One evening about Christmas time, as he and his wife were sitting over the fire chatting together, he said to her, "I should like to sit up and watch to-night, that we may see who it is that comes and does my work for me." The wife liked the thought; so they left a light burning, and hid themselves in the corner of the room behind a curtain and watched to see what would happen.

As soon as it was midnight, there came two little naked dwarfs; and they sat themselves upon the shoemaker's bench, took up all the work that was cut out, and began to ply with their little fingers, stitching and rapping and tapping away at such a rate that the shoemaker was all amazement, and could not take his eyes off for a moment. And on they went till the job was quite finished, and the shoes stood ready for use upon the table. This was long before daybreak; and then they bustled away as quick as lightning.

The next day the wife said to the shoemaker, "These little wights have made us rich, and we ought to be thankful to them, and do them a good office in return. I am quite vexed to see them run about as they do; they have nothing upon their backs to keep off the cold. I'll tell you what, I will make each of them a shirt, and a coat and waistcoat, and a pair of pantaloons into the bargain; do you make each of them a little pair of shoes."

The thought pleased the good shoemaker very much; and one evening, when all the things were ready, they laid them on the table instead of the work that they used to cut out, and then went and hid themselves to watch what the little elves would do.

About midnight the elves came in and were going to sit down to their work as usual; but when they saw the clothes lying for them, they laughed and were greatly delighted. Then they dressed themselves in the twinkling of an eye, and danced and capered and sprang about as merry as could be, till at last they danced out at the door and over the green; and the shoemaker saw them no more; but everything went well with him from that time forward, as long as he lived.

Raccoon

You could introduce the poem by asking the
children what they would wish for on a
lucky star, on a white horse, or with a
wishbone.

Discuss why we are always wishing for
changes, and if we should be satisfied with
what we have in life.

One summer night a little Raccoon,
Above his left shoulder, looked at the new moon.
  He made a wish
  He said: "I wish
  I were a Catfish,
  A Blowfish, a Squid,
  A Katydid,
  A Beetle, a Skink,
  An Ostrich, a pink
  Flamingo, a Gander,
  A Salamander,
  A Hippopotamus,
  A Duck-billed Platypus,
  A Gecko, a Slug,
  A Water Bug,
  A pug-nosed Beaver,
  Anything whatever
Except what I am, a little Raccoon!"

Above his left shoulder, the Evening Star
Listened and heard the little Raccoon
  Who wished on the moon;
  And she said: "Why wish
  You were a Catfish,
  A Blowfish, a Squid,
  A Katydid,
  A Beetle, a Skink,
  An Ostrich, a pink
  Flamingo, a Gander,
  A Salamander,
  A Hippopotamus,
  A Duck-billed Platypus,
  A Gecko, a Slug,
  A Water Bug,
  A pug-nosed Beaver,
  Anything whatever?

Why must you change?" said the Evening Star,
"When you are perfect as you are?
I know a boy who wished on the moon
That *he* might be a little Raccoon!"

WILLIAM JAY SMITH

Here Come Raccoons!

By Lillian Hoban

Before the story

Discuss the wild animals that live in the "city" zoo—creatures that make their homes in an urban setting, e.g. mice, squirrels, raccoons. Ask the children "How do they live? Where do they live? What do they eat? Why aren't they pets?"

During the story

This story is told in three chapters; one chapter can be read each day, so that the class can predict and anticipate what will happen in the subsequent chapter. Before Chapter 1 ask, "What do you think a story called 'Here Come Raccoons' will be about?" Before Chapter 2 reread the line "No twins allowed at Possum Junction." Ask, "Do you think that the twins will stay at home as they were told?" (Be sure to ask the children to clarify and support their answers.) Before Chapter 3 ask, "Do you think the raccoons will get the garbage can open? What will happen when the family learns that Arabella and Albert have come to help with the problem?"

After the story

Have the class retell the story from the viewpoint of the two young raccoons. Help one child begin with "I" and fill in as much of the story as possible, while another child continues as the other twin. You remain "in role" as the story teller.

Chapter 1

Albert and Arabella Raccoon were twins. They looked exactly alike. No one could tell which one was Albert and which one was Arabella. They had the same number of rings on their tails, the same bright look in their beady black eyes, and when they lifted their noses out of their milk mugs, they each had exactly the same milk mustaches.

"It certainly is a trial," sighed Mrs. Raccoon as she mended twin jackets in exactly the same places, "not to be able to tell my own children apart."

Outside, Albert and Arabella were practising opening garbage cans in the backyard. First Albert got on the lid and rocked back and forth. When he got the can rocking hard, Arabella stood on her tiptoes and gave it a shove. The

can fell over with a crash, the lid rolled off, and Albert hopped in.

Mr. Raccoon, who was dozing behind his paper, opened one eye. He let the paper drop on his face as the crash echoed through the house. The night before he had taken advantage of the full moon to go to Possum Junction in search of better garbage cans, and he was very tired. "Tell those twins to stop the noise," he groaned sleepily.

"Beautiful technique," said Grandfather Raccoon, coming up the path. "That was pretty fancy footwork, Albert." He patted Arabella on the back. "You're a credit to your father."

"I'm not Albert, sir, I'm Arabella," said Arabella.

"Hm'm, yes," said Grandfather. He peered at Arabella over his glasses and pinched her cheek. "As I was saying, a credit to your mother."

Mrs. Raccoon came out on the porch. "Children," she called, "stop that racket. Father's trying to take a nap."

"We were only doing our homework, Ma," said Albert. "Teacher said to do three simple can-opening exercises."

"When I was young, Arabella," said Mother, "we girls were taught to do our can opening daintily, without any noise."

"I'm not Arabella, Ma, I'm Albert," said Albert.

"It's just as I was saying to their father," said Mrs. Raccoon to Grandfather. "What's a poor woman to do when she can't tell her own children apart? It does seem hard sometimes," she sighed, "not to be able to tell which is which."

"You mean who is who," said Grandfather kindly. "But don't fret, they'll change with time. Nature's bound to take her course." He settled himself comfortably into a rocking chair and looked fondly at the twins as they helped Mother serve tea.

"Milk or lemon, sir?" asked Albert politely.

"And will you have one of these cream cakes?" asked Arabella.

"Milk, thank you, and I'll have one of the sticky buns," said Grandfather. He took a sip of tea and a bite of sticky bun. "Excellent sticky bun," he murmured. "Best I've had in a long time."

"Father got them over at Possum Junction," said Mother. "They have the best cakes and sticky buns there."

"Well," said Grandfather, "in that case I'll have another. It might be a long time before I get a chance to eat a Possum Junction sticky bun again."

"How's that?" asked Mother.

"What!" said Grandfather. "Haven't you heard the news? The skunks and the possums at Possum Junction have gotten up a petition against us raccoons. They've put up a sign on Main Street saying *No Raccoons Wanted Here.*"

"Why's that?" asked Father who had come out on the porch. "We raccoons have always been good neighbours to the possums and the skunks. When hard times came we always shared with them and they shared with us."

"Well," said Grandfather, "some of the skunks and possums say that the raccoons make such a mess of the garbage that people buy extra fancy garbage cans that are foolproof. No one can get the lids off, and everyone has a hard time."

"Pooh," said Albert. "No can is too hard for a smart raccoon to open."

"I bet we could open any old foolproof can," said Arabella. "We're in the advanced group of our Creative Can-opening Class."

"Quiet twins," said Father thoughtfully. "I'm afraid the skunks and possums are right. I was at Possum Junction last night. And there were quite a few cans that had those newfangled foolproof lids."

"Seems to me the best thing to do would be to fool the foolproof lids," said Mother, her eyes snapping, "instead of turning on your friends and neighbours."

"You're right, Mother," said Father. "But how are you going to get the skunks and possums to see it your way?"

"We could go to Possum Junction tonight when the moon is down," said Mother. We could figure out how to open those newfangled lids!"

"Oh let us help!" cried the twins excitedly.

"Now twins," said Father sternly, "this is grown-up business. Possum Junction is no place for you twins to be fooling around."

"We wouldn't fool around," cried Arabella. "Please let us help!"

"Well . . ." said Father cautiously.

"Look, we have a new technique," said Albert eagerly demonstrating. "Arabella holds the can like this." He held on to the tea table. "I put one foot up." The table tilted dangerously. "Then Arabella jumps. . . ."

"Look out!" cried Grandfather.

The table went over with a crash. Arabella, who was poised to jump, slipped on a cream cake. She skidded into Albert as he crawled out from under the table wearing a plate of sticky buns rakishly over one eye. Albert backed up and bumped into Mother. Arabella was blissfully eating the remains of the cream cake that had stuck to her foot and looked up in smeary surprise as Mother came tumbling down on her. She rolled over on her back, and her legs shot up dislodging the cream cake.

Father, who had been standing braced against the porch rail trying to keep an aloof distance, let out a muffled roar as the cream cake made a direct hit full on his face.

"Aaalbert!" he yelled through the cream, groping in the direction of Arabella.

"I'm not Albert, sir, I'm Arabella," said Arabella, fearfully peering out from behind Mother's skirts.

"I'm Albert, sir," said Albert. He pulled at the sticky buns, and as they suddenly came loose he fell over backwards onto Mother and Arabella.

"I don't care which of you is which!" roared Father wiping gobs of cream from his face. "That settles it! *No twins allowed at Possum Junction!*"

"You mean who is who," said Grandfather. He stared hard at the twins over his glasses. "Someday," he said, "and I hope it's soon, Nature's *bound* to take her course!"

Chapter 2

That night, after the twins had been put safely to bed, Mr. and Mrs. Raccoon and Grandfather made plans to go to Possum Junction when the moon went down.

"We'll have to be very careful," warned Grandfather. "I hear some of the skunks are setting up roadblocks."

Father was busy drawing a map of Possum Junction. "If they are guarding the roads, we'll come in by way of Duckweed Marsh," he said. "We'll come up here over Pinecone Hill," he traced a line with his paw, "and we'll work our way down to Prickle Thorn Corner. That's where I saw all those newfangled cans. With any luck, we'll be able to figure out how to open them, and be back home before the sun rises."

"Then," said Mother with satisfaction, "we can invite all the skunks and possums to a can-opening class. We'll teach them how to open those foolproof lids, we'll have a picnic supper, and we'll all be friends again!"

"Foolproof lids may really be foolproof," warned Grandfather.

"Pooh!" said Father. "No can is too hard for a smart raccoon to open."

There was a curious sound outside the kitchen, half way between a sneeze and a snicker. Albert and Arabella were sneaking past the door and they giggled when they heard Father. They knew who the smart raccoons were, and they were on their way to Possum Junction to prove it. Albert opened the front door, and Arabella very carefully lowered the latch so that it hardly made a sound.

Inside the kitchen, Mother's sharp ears pricked up. "Seems to be a lot of stirring around tonight," she said nervously.

"It's only the wind through the willows," said Father, and they settled themselves to wait for the moon to go down.

Albert and Arabella ran down the path through the woods. They tiptoed past the rabbit hole where Mrs. Rabbit's babies were fast asleep with their noses on their paws.

They skirted the silvery pond where the bullfrogs croaked hoarsely, "Here come Rac—coons."

They glided as smoothly as shadows through the meadow while the owl looking down on them hooted, "Here—come—Rac—coons!" And they trotted hurriedly across the road as the headlights of a car caught the bright shine of their beady black eyes.

When they got to Possum Junction, they did just as they had heard Father say. They sloshed through Duckweed Marsh with the tadpoles and peepers skip-hopping in front of them. They climbed stealthily up Pinecone Hill with the pine needles soft and slippery underfoot. And they worked their way down to Prickle Thorn Corner where all the newfangled cans with the foolproof lids were.

When they got there it was very quiet. Some garbage cans were lined up in a row next to a garage, their foolproof lids locked on tight with handles that stuck up like ears.

The twins sniffed at all of the cans cautiously, and then singled out one that smelled especially good. Then Albert backed off, put his head down, and ran as fast as he could till his head butted *thwock!* against the can. The can went over with a thud but the lid stayed on. Albert pulled and pried at the ear-shaped handles while Arabella got a toehold on the lid and pushed with all her might. It was no use. The lid stayed on. Then the twins ran round and round the can stopping every once in a while and standing on their tiptoes to examine the handles. After a while, they sat down to rest.

"If I had a long flat stick," said Albert thoughtfully, "I could put it through the handle and we would both sit on one end and work it like a seesaw. That way, when the stick went down, the handle would flip open."

Arabella jumped up and down excitedly. "That's what I call a smart raccoon!" she said. "Let's go look for a stick. You look out here, and I'll look inside the garage."

"OK," said Albert, and he ran off to look.

Arabella tiptoed into the garage. She saw a lawnmower, a ladder, an old trunk, and a bicycle. In front of her were some coils of rope, a box of old toys with blocks and dolls and roller skates spilling out, and a large empty pretzel can. In one corner were piles of newspapers, a sled, and some ice skates, and standing against the wall . . . a hockey stick!

Chapter 3

Arabella squeaked in delight and ran forward eagerly to get the stick. In her haste she tripped on the coil of rope that was in front of her and somersaulted head over heels with a loud crash into the box of toys. Arabella lay very still for a moment. The crash had been loud enough for all the skunks and possums in Possum Junction to come and investigate. She pulled herself up cautiously and peered over the edge of the box. All was quiet. Breathing a sigh of relief she stepped backwards out of the box, and immediately her foot was caught in something hard and cold that clamped on tight. Arabella looked down in horror and saw that she was attached to a roller skate. She shook her foot, but the skate stuck fast. She put her foot down hard and shoved.

Woosh! Away she went . . . arms outstretched, tail flying behind . . . *smack!* into the empty pretzel can. The can flew up, looped in the air, and came down *spang!* on her head. Wearing the can like a helmet, Arabella pirouetted gracefully and was flung like a top against the back wall. With a crash that shook the garage, she landed in a heap on the pile of newspapers. In the silence that followed, Arabella could hear far in the distance an angry murmuring.

Just then Albert ran into the garage. "Arabella!" he yelled, "there's a whole troop of skunks and possums coming down the hill. . . . We've got to get the lid off the can fast!" He stopped short and stared at Arabella in amazement. She had pulled herself up and, balancing shakily on her skate, was brandishing the hockey stick like a sword in front of her.

"That's perfect, Arabella," Albert yelled in delight. "Just perfect!" Outside, the angry murmuring was coming closer.

"Quick," cried Arabella, "help me get the skate off."

"There's no time," said Albert. "They've got Mother and Father."

Much closer now, they heard Grandfather's voice, "We only want to show you . . ."

"We'll show *you*!" yelled the skunks and the possums.

"They've got Grandfather too," gasped Arabella.

"You keep a good grip on the hockey stick," yelled Albert, "and aim it right at that garbage can. We'll show those skunks and possums!"

Albert ran in back of Arabella and steered her down the length of the garage. Arabella, zooming along on her roller skate, aimed the hockey stick, business end ready. Faster and faster they flew, wooshing out of the garage into the very midst of the roaring crowd. Arabella struck wildly about her in all directions, clearing a path to the garbage can, sending the terrified skunks and possums flying.

"Get ready," yelled Albert. "Aim . . . *Now!*"

With a sudden twist, Arabella hooked the hockey stick under the foolproof handle of the garbage can and sat down hard, putting all of her weight on the stick. Albert jumped on top of her, adding his weight. The stick went down like a see-saw, and the foolproof handle flipped open! Immediately, the lid spun off and the twins were flung up into the air. They came down into the open garbage can with a thud that sent Arabella's roller skate flying and rattled the pretzel can loose from her head!

For a moment there was absolute silence. Inside the garbage can Arabella gingerly was feeling with her tongue an odd space that had suddenly appeared in her front teeth. She poked her head out of the can as Father, holding the lid of the foolproof garbage can aloft, said proudly to the startled skunks and possums, "I told you no can was too hard for a smart raccoon to open!" He reached over and patted Arabella on the head. "Albert," he said, "you twins did a fine job!"

"I'm not Albert, sir, I'm Arabella," said Arabella, and she grinned to show off the space where her front tooth had come out.

Albert poked his head out of the can. "I'm Albert, sir," he said.

Grandfather, standing at the edge of the crowd with Mother, looked hard at Albert. Then he stared at Arabella. "I told you," he said turning to Mother, "I told you all along! I told you that Nature was bound to take her course!"

That evening, the skunks and possums came to the twins' house for a can-opening class. Afterwards they all had a picnic supper. There were potato salad and baked beans, cole slaw and meat loaf, hot dogs and corn on the cob, relish and pickles, root beer, lemonade, and pitchers of cool foamy milk. For dessert there were the famous Possum Junction cream cakes and sticky buns. Arabella and Albert sat in the place of honour at the head of the picnic table.

Grandfather got up, cleared his throat and said, "Friends and neighbours, I have an announcement to make. Starting next week we will open a new sporting goods shop featuring foolproof garbage can openers. You'll be able to get a small, inexpensive model, or a special jumbo model with your name on it. Mother will be head sales lady, and I will be general manager. Father will be doing the whittling with the help of the twins. We guarantee that all the openers will work perfectly or your money back!"

A cheer went up from the crowd. Grandfather cleared his throat again. "If the twins can stop eating and drinking for a minute," he said looking at them fondly, "Now we can tell which is which. . . ."

"You mean who is who," whispered Mother.

"Yes," said Grandfather, "now that we can tell Arabella from Albert, I'd like to introduce the talented young designers of the New Foolproof Garbage Can Opener. Arabella your turn first."

Arabella lifted her nose out of her milk mug and stood up and curtsied and grinned.

Grandfather peered over his glasses at the space between her front teeth. "Now your turn, Albert."

Albert lifted his nose out of his milk mug. Then he took a last bite of sticky bun. An odd look came into his beady black eyes and he swallowed very hard. Then he stood up and bowed and grinned.

"Oh no!" said Grandfather sinking into his chair. "Oh no!"

For there, side by side, stood the twins looking exactly alike again. . . . The same number of rings on their tails, the same bright look in their beady black eyes, the same milk mustaches, and when they grinned, exactly the same space in their front teeth where a loose tooth had come out!

Ranzo

Read this poem with two different voices,
one for asking the questions and the other
for whispering the answers. Try reading
the last line as if you have a cold.

What problems have different pets caused
for the children in the class? Try to rephrase
each story the children tell into questions
and answers, like the poem.

Who rolled in the mud
behind the garage door?
Who left footprints
across the kitchen floor?

I know a dog whose nose is cold
I know a dog whose nose is cold

Who chased raindrops
down the windows?
Who smudged the glass
with the end of his nose?

I know a dog with a cold in his nose
I know a dog with a cold in his nose

Who wants a bath
and a big crunchy biscuit?
Who wants to bed down
in his fireside basket?

Me, said Ranzo
I'm the dog with a cold.

MICHAEL ROSEN

What's in Fox's Sack?

RETOLD BY PAUL GALDONE

Before the story

Ask the children what kinds of secrets they have been asked to keep. Discuss why it is so difficult not to peek at birthday gifts or Christmas gifts.

After the story

Can the children remember the sequence of events in the story? Do they know any other stories like this one (e.g., Red Riding Hood)?

Fill a sack (or a bag) with interestingly shaped objects. Can the children identify them by feeling them through the sack?

One day Fox was digging by his tree stump when he found a big fat bumblebee. So he put it in his sack. Then he walked, and he walked, and he walked, till he came to a house.

In the house there was a very little woman sweeping the floor.

"Good morning," said Fox.

"Good morning," said the very little woman.

"May I leave my sack here?" asked Fox. "I want to go to my friend Squintum's house."

"Yes, certainly," the very little woman replied.

"Very well, then," said Fox. "But mind you don't look in the sack!"

"Oh, I won't," said the very little woman.

So off went Fox, trot, trot, trot-trot-trot, to Squintum's house.

As soon as he was gone, the very little woman *did* look in the sack. She just peeped in, and out flew the big fat bumblebee! And the very little woman's rooster ran and gobbled him up.

Presently, back came Fox. He looked in his sack and he said, "Where is my big fat bumblebee?"

And the very little woman said, "I'm very sorry, but I'm afraid I *did* look in your sack,

and the big fat bumblebee flew out, and my rooster gobbled him up."

"Oh, really?" said Fox. "Then I shall take your rooster instead."

So he caught the very little woman's rooster and put him in the sack. Then off he went.

He walked, and he walked, and he walked, till he came to another house.

In this house there was a very big woman darning socks.

"Good morning," said Fox.

"Good morning," said the very big woman.

"May I leave my sack here while I go to my friend Squintum's house?" Fox asked.

"Yes, certainly," the very big woman replied.

"Very well, then," said Fox. "But mind you don't look in the sack!"

"Oh, I won't," said the very big woman.

So off went Fox, trot, trot, trot-trot-trot, to Squintum's house.

As soon as he was gone, the very big woman *did* look in the sack. She just peeped in, and out flew the rooster. And the very big woman's pig chased him down the lane.

Presently, back came Fox. He looked in his sack and he said, "Oho! Where is my rooster?"

And the very big woman said, "I'm very sorry, but I *did* open your sack. And your rooter flew out, and my pig chased him down the lane."

"Very well," said Fox. "I shall take your pig instead." So he caught the very big woman's pig and put him in the sack. Then off he went.

He walked, and he walked, and he walked, till he came to another house.

In this house there was a very skinny woman washing the dishes.

"Good morning," said Fox.

"Good morning," said the very skinny woman.

"May I leave my sack here while I go to my friend Squintum's house?" Fox asked.

"Yes, certainly," the very skinny woman replied.

"Very well, then," said Fox. "But mind you don't look in the sack!"

"Oh, I won't," said the very skinny woman.

So off went Fox, trot, trot, trot-trot-trot, to Squintum's house.

As soon as he was gone, the very skinny woman *did* look in the sack. She just peeped in, and out jumped the pig. And the very skinny woman's little boy took a stick and chased him out of the house.

Presently, back came Fox. He looked in his sack and he said, "Where is my pig?"

And the very skinny woman said, "I'm very sorry, but I'm afraid I *did* look in your sack. And the pig jumped out, and my little boy took a stick and chased him out of the house."

"My goodness," said Fox. "Then I shall have to take your little boy instead." And he took the very skinny woman's little boy and put him in the sack. Then off he went.

He walked, and he walked, and he walked, till he came to another house.

And in this house there was a very fat woman making gingerbread. At one side of her sat three little girls. And on the other side sat a big watchdog.

"Good morning," said Fox.

"Good morning," said the very fat woman.

"May I leave my sack here while I go to my friend Squintum's house?" Fox asked.

"Yes, certainly," the very fat woman replied.

"Very well, then," said Fox. "But mind you don't look in the sack!"

"Oh, I won't," said the very fat woman.

Then off went Fox, trot, trot, trot-trot-trot, to Squintum's house.

Now as soon as he was gone, the lovely smell of the gingerbread came out of the oven. It smelled so good that all the three little girls called out, "Oh, Mother, Mother, may we have some gingerbread?"

And the little boy in the sack called out, "Oh, may I have some gingerbread, too?"

Well, of course, as soon as the very fat woman heard a little boy calling from the sack, she undid it at once. And out climbed the little boy. And so that Fox wouldn't notice anything, the very fat woman put the big watchdog in the sack instead.

Presently, back came Fox. He looked at the sack, and it still looked as full as before. So he picked it up and off he went.

He walked, and he walked, and he walked, till he came to a forest. There he stopped to rest. He put down the sack and said, "It is almost dinnertime. That little boy will make a very good meal for me!" And he untied the sack.

Out jumped *not* the little boy, but the BIG WATCHDOG. Fox was so frightened that he ran away as fast as he could.

When the big watchdog got back home, the very fat woman was just taking the gingerbread out of the oven. She gave pieces to the three little girls and the little boy. And she gave an especially *big* piece to the watchdog.

Imagine

After reading the poem to the children,
have them describe the strange-sized
creatures the poem describes. Ask, "What
problems would arise if these new creatures
existed?"

Imagine a snail
As big as a whale,
Imagine a lark
As big as a shark,
Imagine a cat
As small as a gnat
And a bee as big as a tree.

Imagine a toad
As long as a road,
Imagine a hare
As big as a chair,
Imagine a goat
As long as a boat
And a flea the same size as me.

ROLAND EGAN

Tikki Tikki Tembo

RETOLD BY ARLENE MOSEL

Before the story

The children can discuss the nicknames of various members of their family. As well, they can repeat their full names aloud, and if possible, explain why they were given these names by their parents.

After the story

Ask if anyone can repeat the full name of the mischievous boy.

Discuss the reasons why some children play where they are not supposed to play.

Have the class invent a perfect playground for parents and for children. Ask, for example, "Will there be a place to swim? Will there be trees to climb? Will there be valleys to run in? Will there be jungle vines to swing on?"

Once upon a time, a long, long time ago, it was the custom of all the fathers and mothers in China to give their first and honoured sons great long names. But second sons were given hardly any name at all.

In a small mountain village there lived a mother who had two little sons. Her second son she called Chang, which meant "little or nothing." But her first and honoured son, she called Tikki tikki tembo-no sa rembo-chari bari ruchi-pip peri pembo, which meant "the most wonderful thing in the whole wide world!"

Every morning the mother went to wash in a little stream near her home. The two boys always went chattering along with her. On the bank was an old well.

"Don't go near the well," warned the mother, "or you will surely fall in."

The boys did not always mind their mother and one day they were playing beside the well, and on the well when Chang fell in!

Tikki tikki tembo-no sa rembo-chari bari ruchi-pip peri pembo ran as fast as his little legs could carry him to his mother and said, "Most Honourable Mother, Chang has fallen into the well!"

"The water roars, 'Little Blossom,' I cannot hear you," said the mother.

Then Tikki tikki tembo-no sa rembo-chari bari ruchi-pip peri pembo raised his voice and cried, "Oh, Most Honourable One, Chang has fallen into the well!"

"That troublesome boy," answered the mother. "Run and get the Old Man with the Ladder to fish him out."

Then Tikki tikki tembo-no sa rembo-chari bari ruchi-pip peri pembo ran as fast as his little legs could carry him to the Old Man with the Ladder and said, "Old Man with the Ladder, Chang has fallen into the well. Will you come and fish him out?"

"So," said the Old Man with the Ladder, "Chang has fallen into the well."

And he ran as fast as his old legs could carry him. Step over step, step over step he went into the well, picked up little Chang, and step over step, step over step brought him out of the well.

He pumped the water out of him and pushed the air into him, and pumped the water out of him and pushed the air into him, and soon Chang was just as good as ever!

Now for several months the boys did not go near the well. But after the Festival of the Eighth Moon they ran to the well to eat their rice cakes.

They ate near the well, they played around the well, they walked on the well and Tikki tikki tembo-no sa rembo-chari bari ruchi-pip peri pembo fell into the well!

Chang ran as fast as his little legs could carry him to his mother and said, "Oh, Most Honourable Mother, Tikki tikki tembo-no sa rembo-chari bari ruchi-pip peri pembo has fallen into the well!"

"The water roars, 'Little One,' I cannot hear you."

So little Chang took a deep breath. "Oh, Mother, Most Honourable," he panted, "Tikki tikki tembo-no sa rembo-chari bari ruchi-pip peri pembo has fallen into the well!"

"Tiresome Child, what are you trying to say?" said his mother.

"Honourable Mother!
Chari bari
rembo
tikki tikki,"
he gasped,
"pip pip
has fallen into the well!"

"Unfortunate Son, surely the evil spirits have bewitched your tongue. Speak your brother's name with reverence."

Poor little Chang was all out of breath from saying that great long name, and he didn't think he could say it one more time. But then he thought of his brother in the old well.

Chang bowed his little head clear to the sand, took a deep breath and slowly, very slowly said, "Most Honourable Mother, Tikki tikki—tembo-no—sa rembo—chari bari—ruchi-pip—peri pembo is at the bottom of the well."

"Oh, not my first and honoured son, heir of all I possess! Run quickly and tell the Old Man with the Ladder that your brother has fallen into the well."

So Chang ran as fast as his little legs would carry him to the Old Man with the Ladder. Under a tree the Old Man with the Ladder sat bowed and silent.

"Old Man, Old Man," shouted Chang. "Come right away! Tikki tikki tembo-no sa rembo-chari bari ruchi-pip peri pembo has fallen into the stone well!"

But there was no answer. Puzzled he waited. Then with his very last bit of breath he shouted, "Old Man with the Ladder, Tikki tikki tembo-no sa rembo-chari bari ruchi-pip peri pembo is at the bottom of the well."

"Miserable child, you disturb my dream. I had floated into a purple mist and found my youth again. There were glittering gateways and jeweled blossoms. If I close my eyes perhaps I will again return."

Poor little Chang was frightened. How could he say that great long name again? "Please, Old Man with the Ladder, please help my brother out of the cold well."

"So," said the Old Man with the Ladder, "your mother's 'Precious Pearl' has fallen into the well!"

The Old Man with the Ladder hurried as fast as his old legs could carry him. Step over step, step over step he went into the well, and step over step, step over step out of the well with the little boy in his arms. Then he pumped the water out of him and pushed the air into him, and pumped the water out of him and pushed the air into him.

But little Tikki tikki tembo-no sa rembo-chari bari ruchi-pip peri pembo had been in the water so long, all because of his great long name, that the moon rose many times before he was quite the same again.

And from that day to this the Chinese have always thought it wise to give all their children little, short names instead of great long names.

Some One

This quiet, gentle poem has a wonderful
quality of suspense, and should be read in a
whisper, hinting at the unknown visitor.
The children can suggest who the visitor
might have been and why they left before
the knock was answered.

Ask the children, "What other sounds
were heard at the same time?"

Some one came knocking
　　At my wee, small door;
Some one came knocking,
　　I'm sure—sure—sure;

I listened, I opened,
　　I looked to left and right,
But nought there was a-stirring
　　In the still dark night;

Only the busy beetle
　　Tap-tapping in the wall,
Only from the forest
　　The screech-owl's call,

Only the cricket whistling
　　While the dewdrops fall,
So I know not who came knocking,
　　At all, at all, at all.

WALTER DE LA MARE

Little Sister and the Month Brothers

RETOLD BY BEATRICE SCHENK DE REGNIERS

Before the story

Have each child give the date of his/her birthday and categorize them on the blackboard or chart by months.

Ask, "Which season is your birthday month in?"

Regroup the months by the four seasons.

Introduce the title of the story and have the children predict the story line.

During the story

Read the dialogue lines in character, since they are only fragments of meaning.

After the story

Ask, "How did each of the twelve Month Brothers help Little Sister?" Relate the answers to the seasons as the children remember and understand them. (A cut out, such as a strawberry, could symbolically represent each month or season.)

The children could draw the Month Brother that represents their birthday month.

Well, there was this girl. We don't know her name, but everyone called her Little Sister. Her mother was dead, and so was her father. She lived with her stepmother and stepsister in a little cottage near a dark forest.

This was once upon a time, in the days when stepmothers were wicked and stepsisters were mean and lazy.

Little Sister had to do all the work in the house.

She had to do all the work outside the house too—in the meadow and in the garden. And every morning and every evening, she milked the cow.

The stepmother and the stepsister never said thank you to Little Sister. All day long they hollered and they grumbled and they complained.

"Come in, stupid, and make me some tea!"

"Hurry up, stupid!"

"This tea is too hot, stupid."

"This tea is too weak, stupid."

"Come in this minute and sew a button on my dress."

But Little Sister did not seem to mind. Most of the time she sang or hummed while she worked. And every day Little Sister grew prettier and prettier.

The stepmother and stepsister couldn't stand seeing Little Sister looking happier and prettier day after day.

What if a young man were to come by? He might choose Little Sister for a wife instead of the stepsister!

The stepmother and stepsister made up their minds to get rid of Little Sister.

The stepsister looked out of the window. It was bitter cold outside. Snow covered the ground. Now the stepsister knew how to get rid of Little Sister! She would send her out in the cold to look for fresh violets.

"Little Sister! Come here this minute."

"Yes, Stepsister. What do you want?"

"I want you to go to the forest and pick a bunch of violets for me."

"Violets in January? Dear Stepsister, you are joking!"

"I am not joking. Go!"

The stepmother thought this was a very good idea. She pushed Little Sister outside and told her not to come back without fresh violets. Then she slammed the door shut and locked it. Poor Little Sister did not even have a coat on.

"Brrr. I know violets grow in the forest . . . but not in January. Not under all this snow."

How cold it was. Just when Little Sister thought she could not take one more step, she saw a light shining high above the trees.

"A light! Courage! I must go on."

31

She walked toward the light.

Soon she reached a huge rock. She could see that the light came from a fire burning way on top.

"Courage! I must climb this rock."

She managed to climb the rock.

Twelve men were standing in a circle around a big fire. Three of the men had long white hair and long white beards. They wore fur capes, white as snow.

Three were very young men—almost boys. One of them wore a brown velvet cape lined with green silk. The other two were dressed all in green. Three were full-grown men. They looked tall and strong, and their capes were of green and gold. The last three men had brown beards and wore woolen capes of gold and brown.

Little Sister knew at once that these were the twelve Month Brothers.

Brother January asked Little Sister what she wanted. Very politely, Little Sister asked if she could come near the fire and warm herself. Then she explained that she had come to gather violets, and that she dare not go home without them.

"Violets in January? Go home, Little Sister. Come back in April."

"I dare not go home without violets. My stepmother will kill me."

Brother January told the Month Brothers they must all help Little Sister.

January passed his staff to Brother February. An icy wind began to blow. Quickly February gave the staff to a young man standing next to him.

"Take it, Brother March."

As March held the staff, the snow melted on the ground, and a patch of muddy earth could be seen. Soon there was a hint of green grass.

March smiled and said to the young man next to him, dressed all in green from head to toe: "Take the staff, Brother April. Only you can give us violets."

Brother April took the staff and whirled it above his head. There was a shower of warm rain. Then all the tree branches nearby put out green leaves.

Grass appeared, and the muddy brown earth turned green.

Now, in a circle around Brother April, there was a carpet of blue violets.

Little Sister quickly filled her apron with the sweet-smelling violets. She thanked the Month Brothers and ran home.

When Little Sister brought home the violets, the stepmother and stepsister were astonished. The sweet smell of violets filled the house. But no one thanked Little Sister. The stepmother told her to get back to work. The stepsister was thinking of a way to get rid of Little Sister.

The next day, the stepsister waited until supper was over and it was dark outside. Then she told Little Sister to go out and gather fresh strawberries. The stepmother gave Little Sister a basket and pushed her out the door. She told her not to come back until the basket was filled with strawberries.

Little Sister ran to keep from freezing. At last she reached the rock and climbed it.

The Month Brothers were there, standing in a circle around the fire. Little Sister greeted them politely and told them why she had come.

"Good evening, Month Brothers. I must bring strawberries to my stepsister."

"Someone is very greedy."

"Only Brother June can give us strawberries."

Once more the staff was passed—from January to February, from February to March to April to May, and at last to Brother June.

As the staff went from Month Brother to Month Brother, once again the seasons changed and the earth became green and blossoming.

Little Sister saw the white, star-shaped blossoms appear in the green grass—and fade. Then she saw the green berries grow and ripen to red.

June warned Little Sister to hurry. He told her she could gather five berries.

"Hurry, Little Sister. You may gather five berries. Then it will be winter again."

Quickly Little Sister gathered the berries, thanked the Month Brothers, and ran home.

The stepmother and stepsister looked at the basket greedily. When they saw only five strawberries, they were angry.

"What? Only five berries!"

"Oh you cheater!"

"You ate them! You ate all but these five berries."

They would not believe Little Sister when she told them the Month Brothers would not let her pick more than five berries.

The stepsister and stepmother ate the five strawberries, one after the other. They had never tasted anything so delicious!

The stepsister made up her mind to get a basket full of those delicious strawberries.

"Which Month Brother gave them to you?"

"Brother June. But Stepsister—"

"No one can stop me!"

She put on her fur-lined cape and hood. She put on her fur-lined boots and her fur-lined mittens, and she ran out to find the Month Brothers.

Even with all her warm clothes the stepsister began to feel cold. When she saw the light, she ran toward it and climbed the rock.

"Brrr. That must be the fire of the Month Brothers."

She pushed her way past the Month Brothers to warm herself at the fire. When January asked why she had come, the stepsister told him it was none of his business. She said she would speak only to Brother June.

"You do, do you? Well, just try to find him now."

January was angry. He swung his staff in the air. The wind blew. The snow fell thick and fast.

The stepsister could no longer see the fire or the Month Brothers. She stumbled along in the snow, trying to find her way home.

The stepmother, waiting at home, was worried. At last she decided to go out to look for the stepsister.

"I must find her."

Little Sister waited and waited for the stepmother and the stepsister to come home. But they never came back. No one ever saw them again.

"They must be lost forever."

Now Little Sister had the cottage to herself, and the garden and the meadow and the cow.

Little Sister worked as hard as ever. But now there was no one to holler or grumble or complain.

The only sound in the house was the sound of Little Sister singing to herself. She was lonely sometimes.

One day an honest farmer came to the door and asked Little Sister to marry him, and she did.

Little Sister was no longer lonely. The farmer was very fond of her, and he helped her with the work.

Sometimes the farmer hollered or grumbled or complained, but not very often.

Sometimes, on snowy winter evenings, Little Sister would look out of the window and remember the twelve Month Brothers.

And the Month Brothers never forgot Little Sister. The spring flowers came early to the meadow. And the fruits and vegetables in the garden were always the first and the finest. In the wintertime, the snow drifted into a wall around the house and garden to protect them from the cold wind.

All went well for Little Sister and her husband, and they lived together in peace and happiness.

Us Two

Ask the children to describe their favorite
possession—a special blanket, a baseball
cap, a teddy bear. Explain that Pooh was
Christopher Robin's teddy bear.
Christopher Robin, however, thought Pooh
was his best friend and talked to him as
if he was a real person. Read the poem to
the class, then discuss the things that Pooh
and Christopher Robin enjoyed doing
together.

Wherever I am, there's always Pooh,
There's always Pooh and Me.
Whatever I do, he wants to do,
"Where are you going to-day?" says
    Pooh:
"Well, that's very odd 'cos I was too.
Let's go together," says Pooh, says he.
"Let's go together," says Pooh.

"What's twice eleven?" I said to Pooh.
("Twice what?" said Pooh to Me.)
"I *think* it ought to be twenty-two."
"Just what I think myself," said Pooh.
"It wasn't an easy sum to do,
But that's what it is," said Pooh, said
    he.
"That's what it is," said Pooh.

"Let's look for dragons," I said to Pooh.
"Yes, let's," said Pooh to Me.
We crossed the river and found a few—
"Yes, those are dragons all right," said
    Pooh.
"As soon as I saw their beaks I knew.

That's what they are," said Pooh, said
    he.
"That's what they are," said Pooh.

"Let's frighten the dragons," I said to
    Pooh.
"That's right," said Pooh to Me.
"*I'm* not afraid," I said to Pooh,
And I held his paw and I shouted "Shoo!
Silly old dragons!"—and off they flew.
"I wasn't afraid," said Pooh, said he,
"I'm *never* afraid with you."

So wherever I am, there's always Pooh,
There's always Pooh and Me.
"What would I do?" I said to Pooh,
"If it wasn't for you," and Pooh said:
    "True,
It isn't much fun for One, but Two
Can stick together," says Pooh, says he.
"That's how it is," says Pooh.

A.A. MILNE

How Rabbit Stole the Fire

JOANNA TROUGHTON

Before the story

Discuss the concept of a "trickster"—
someone who plays tricks on people (e.g.
Bugs Bunny, the Pink Panther).
 Do people like "tricksters" for friends?

After the story

The children could role-play the animals.
Taking a role yourself, question them about
their part in taking the fire. You might
want to talk about fire safety, and why
animals must be protected from fire.

In the beginning there was no fire on Earth, and the world was cold.
 The Sky People had fire. But they lived high up in the mountains, and guarded it from the animals.

"Who will steal the fire?" asked the animals, when the leaves began to fall and the cold winds blew.

The bison was strong. The wolf was cunning. The bear was brave. The wildcat was fierce. But Rabbit was leader of them all in mischief.

Rabbit made himself a wonderful head-dress. Each feather, every stitch he coated with pine resin.

"Here I go," said Rabbit, putting on the wonderful head-dress. And off he went to the village of the Sky People. As he went he sang a song. "Oh, I am going to fetch the fire, to fetch the fire, to fetch the fire." For that is what he was going to do.

"Here is Rabbit," muttered the Sky People. "He is a liar. He is a trickster. He is the chief mischief-maker. Do not trust him."

"Hallo, Sky People," said Rabbit. "I have come to teach you a new dance. Look at my dancing hat. It is a dance to bring the corn from the earth. It is a dance to guide the fish to your nets."

So spoke Rabbit the trickster. And with his words he soothed the Sky People. He charmed them. He flattered them. They forgot that he was a mischief-maker and welcomed him into their village.

"Rabbit shall lead us in the dance!"

So Rabbit led the dance! Round and round the fire danced Rabbit. And round and round behind him danced the Sky People. Round and round danced Rabbit, wearing his wonderful head-dress . . . and as he danced, he bent low to the fire, singing his dancing song. And the Sky People bent low also. Round and round danced Rabbit, and very low he bent. . . . Whoosh! The head-dress was alight! And away raced Rabbit, out of the village and down the mountain.

"We have been tricked!" screamed the Sky People. "Rabbit has stolen the fire!"

Rabbit ran and the Sky People followed. They made a great rain. They made thunder and lightning. They made sleet. They made snow. But the wonderful head-dress with the resin-coated feathers burned brightly.

Rabbit was soon tired. "Squirrel! Take the head-dress," he gasped. Squirrel took the head-dress and ran.

As she went, the heat made her tail curl up and over her back. And so are squirrels to this day.

Squirrel was soon tired. "Crow! Take the head-dress," she chattered. Crow took the head-

35

dress and flew. As he went, the smoke turned all his feathers black. And so are crows to this day.

Crow was soon tired. "Raccoon! Take the head-dress," he cawed. Raccoon took the head-dress and ran. As she went, some ash burned rings around her tail and face. And so are raccoons to this day.

Raccoon was soon tired. "Turkey! Take the head-dress," she panted. Turkey took the head-dress and ran. As he went, the fire burned all the feathers off his head and neck. And so are turkeys to this day.

But Turkey was not a fast runner, and the fire began to die.

"Set my tail alight," said Deer. For in those days deer had long tails.

Deer took the fire on her tail, and ran so fast that she made a wind to fan the flames. Deer cried to the trees as she passed, flicking her tail this way and that, "Trees, hide the fire!"

The trees took the fire and hid it in their wood. But the fire had burned off most of Deer's tail. And so are deer to this day.

The Sky People returned to their village high in the mountains. Wood had hidden fire and they didn't know how to find it again.

But Rabbit, leader of all mischief, knew. It was he who showed the animals how to find fire again by rubbing two sticks together.

Now the animals have fire to warm the cold winters, and light to brighten the dark nights.

A Was Once an Apple-Pie

This poem has wonderful, invented rhyme
words (e.g. pidy, widy, tidy, pidy). After
you have read it to the children, have them
replace the rhyme words on the second
read-through.

A was once an apple-pie,
  Pidy,
  Widy,
  Tidy,
  Pidy,
Nice insidy,
Applie-pie!

B was once a little bear,
  Beary,
  Wary,
  Hairy,
  Beary,
Taky cary,
Little bear!

C was once a little cake,
  Caky,
  Baky,
  Maky,
  Caky,
Taky caky,
Little cake!

D was once a little doll,
  Dolly,
  Molly,
  Polly,
  Nolly,
Nursy dolly,
Little doll!

E was once a little eel,
  Eely,
  Weely,
  Peely,
  Eely,
Twirly, tweely,
Little eel!

F was once a little fish,
  Fishy,
  Wishy,
  Squishy,
  Fishy,
In a dishy,
Little fish!

G was once a little goose,
  Goosy,
  Moosy,
  Boosey,
  Goosey,
Waddly-woosy,
Little goose!

H was once a little hen,
  Henny,
  Chenny,
  Tenny,
  Henny,
Eggsy-any,
Little hen?

I was once a bottle of ink,
  Inky,
  Dinky,
  Thinky,
  Inky,
Blacky minky,
Bottle of ink!

J was once a jar of jam,
  Jammy,
  Mammy,
  Clammy,
  Jammy,
Sweety, swammy,
Jar of jam!

K was once a little kite,
  Kity,
  Whity,
  Flighty,
  Kity,
Out of sighty,
Little kite!

L was once a little lark,
  Larky,
  Marky,
  Harky,
  Larky,
In the parky,
Little lark!

M was once a little mouse,
    Mousy,
    Bousy,
    Sousy,
    Mousy,
    In the housy,
    Little mouse!

N was once a little needle,
    Needly,
    Tweedly,
    Threedly,
    Needly,
    Wisky, wheedly,
    Little needle!

O was once a little owl,
    Owly,
    Prowly,
    Howly,
    Owly,
    Browny fowly,
    Little owl!

P was once a little pump,
    Pumpy,
    Slumpy,
    Flumpy,
    Pumpy,
    Dumpy, thumpy,
    Little pump!

Q was once a little quail,
    Quaily,
    Faily,
    Daily,
    Quaily,
    Stumpy-taily,
    Little quail!

R was once a little rose,
    Rosy,
    Posy,
    Nosy,
    Rosy,
    Blows-y, grows-y,
    Little rose!

S was once a little shrimp,
    Shrimpy,
    Nimpy,
    Flimpy,
    Shrimpy,
    Jumpy, jimpy,
    Little shrimp!

T was once a little thrush,
    Thrushy,
    Hushy,
    Bushy,
    Thrushy,
    Flitty, flushy,
    Little thrush!

U was once a little urn,
    Urny,
    Burny,
    Turny,
    Urny,
    Bubbly, burny,
    Little urn!

V was once a little vine,
    Viny,
    Winy,
    Twiny,
    Viny,
    Twisty-twiny,
    Little vine!

W was once a whale,
    Whaly,
    Scaly,
    Shaly,
    Whaly,
    Tumbly-taily,
    Mighty whale!

X was once a great king Xerxes,
    Xerxy,
    Perxy,
    Turxy,
    Xerxy,
    Linxy, lurxy,
    Great King Xerxes!

Y was once a little yew,
    Yewdy,
    Fewdy,
    Crudy,
    Yewdy,
    Growdy, grewdy,
    Little yew!

Z was once a piece of zinc,
    Tinky,
    Winky,
    Blinky,
    Tinky,
    Tinky minky,
    Piece of zinc!

EDWARD LEAR

Hildilid's Night

BY CHELI DURAN RYAN

Before the story

Discuss the concept of "night." Ask the children, "When do you enjoy the night? When do you become annoyed with the night?"

After the story

1. Assist the children in listing the activities Hildilid carried out in order to drive the night from the village of Hexham.
2. Read the story aloud and have the children, all at the same time, mime the actions of Hildilid. (Caution them that in "spat," they will only pretend.)

High in the hills near Hexham there lived an old woman named Hildilid.

She hated bats and owls and moles and voles and moths and stars and shadows and sleep, and even the moonlight, all because she hated the night.

"If only," said Hildilid to her old wolfhound, "I could chase the night from Hexham, the sun would always shine on my hut. I do not know why no one has thought of chasing away the night before."

Hildilid cut a broom from twigs to sweep the night out of her hut and over the hills of Hexham.

She swept and scrubbed and scoured and whisked, but whenever she looked out of her window, the night was still there, like dust behind rafters.

Hildilid pulled out her needle and sewed sackcloth into a strong sack to see if she could fill it with the night and empty it beyond the hills of Hexham.

She wadded and padded and pushed and stuffed, and she even sneaked up on the shadows, but she could not cram all the night into a sack.

Hildilid dragged her heaviest cauldron to the fire so she could boil away the night. She ladled it, stirred it, simmered it, bubbled it, tasted it, and burned it, but she could not boil away the night.

Hildilid gathered vines to tie the night up into a neat bundle.

"Perhaps someone will buy it in the market," she thought.

But she could not tie up the night.

Hildilid sheared the night like a sheep, but all that dropped from the sky was a little cloud.

She tossed the night to her old wolfhound stretched on the rushes, but he could not wolf down the night.

She tucked the night into her straw bed, but it jumped out.

She ducked the night in the well behind her hovel, but it bobbed up.

She singed the night with a candle, but it skipped outside.

Hildilid sang it lullabies, poured it a saucer of milk, shook her fist at it, smoked it in the chimney, stamped on it, spanked it, dug a grave for it, and she even—I am sorry to say—spat at the night.

But the night took no notice.

"Then I shan't notice the night," sniffed old Hildilid, and she turned her back on it.

At that moment the sun climbed over the hills of Hexham. But Hildilid was too tired from fighting the night to enjoy the day.

She settled down to sleep in her straw bed so she would be all fresh and ready to turn her back on the night when it returned to Hexham. . . .

Good Night

Snow

We'll play in the snow
And stray in the snow
And stay in the snow
In a snow-white park.
We'll clown in the snow
And frown in the snow
Fall down in the snow
Till it's after dark.
We'll cook snow pies
In a big snow pan.
We'll make snow eyes
In a round snow man.
We'll sing snow songs
And chant snow chants
And roll in the snow
In our fat snow pants.
And when it's time to go home to eat
We'll have snow toes
On our frosted feet.

KARLA KUSKIN

The Lad Who Went to the North Wind

By Anne Rockwell

Before the story

Discuss any stories the children remember
about magic objects (e.g. lanterns,
wishbones, shoes, beanstalks, etc.). Explain
that this story will concern three magic
objects and someone who tries to steal
them.

After the story

Draw a picture, with the children, of the
North Wind's house and what life would
have been like there (e.g. What rooms
would there be? What would he eat?).

Once upon a time there was a widow who
had one son, and he went out to the
storehouse to fetch some oatmeal for
cooking. But as he was coming back to the
house, there came the North Wind, puffing and
blowing. The North Wind caught up the
oatmeal and blew it away. Then the lad went
back to the storehouse for more, but no sooner
had he come outside than the North Wind came
and blew away the oatmeal with just one puff.
Worse yet, the Wind did it a third time.

At this the lad got very angry, and as he
thought it mean that the North Wind should
behave so, he decided he'd go and find the
North Wind and ask him to give back the
oatmeal.

So off he went, but the way was long, and he
walked and he walked, but at last he came to
the North Wind's house.

"Good day," said the lad. "Thank you for
coming to see us yesterday."

"Good day!" answered the North Wind in a
loud, gruff voice. "Thanks for coming to see me.
What do you want?"

"Oh," said the lad, "I only wished to ask
you to be so kind as to let me have back that
oatmeal you took from me, for my mother and I
haven't much to live on. If you're to go on
snapping up every morsel we have, we'll
starve."

"I haven't got your oatmeal," said the North
Wind, "but if you are in such need, I'll give
you a cloth which will give you all the food you
want if you will only say, 'Cloth, cloth, spread
yourself and serve up a good dinner!' "

With this the lad was happy. But as the way
was so long he couldn't get home in one day,
so he stopped overnight at an inn. He went to
sit down to supper, and he laid the cloth on a
table and said, "Cloth, cloth, spread yourself
and serve up a good dinner!"

And the cloth did.

Everyone at the inn thought this was a
wonderful thing, but most of all the landlady.
So when everyone was fast asleep, she took the
lad's cloth and put another in its place. It looked
just like the one the lad had got from the North
Wind, but it couldn't serve up even a bit of
stale bread.

When the lad woke, he took his cloth and
went home to his mother.

"Now," said he, "I've been to the North
Wind's house, and a good fellow he is. He gave
me this cloth, and when I say to it, 'Cloth,
cloth, spread yourself and serve up a good
dinner!' I can get all the food I want."

"Seeing is believing," said his mother. "I
shan't believe it until I see it."

So the lad made haste, and laid the cloth on
the table. Then he said, "Cloth, cloth, spread

yourself and serve up a good dinner!"

But the cloth served up nothing, not even a bit of stale bread.

"Well," said the lad, "there is nothing to do but to go to the North Wind again." And away he went.

So he walked and he walked, and late in the afternoon he came to where the North Wind lived.

"Good evening," said the lad.

"Good evening," said the North Wind in a loud, gruff voice.

"I want my rights for that oatmeal of ours you took," said the lad. "As for the cloth I got from you, it isn't worth a penny."

"I've got no oatmeal," said the North Wind. "But I'll give you a goat which gives forth golden coins whenever you say to it, 'Goat, goat, make money!' "

So the lad thought this a fine thing, but it was too far to get home that day, so he turned in for the night at the same inn where he had slept before.

When he was settled, he tried out the goat the North Wind had given him and found it all right, but when the landlord saw the goat give forth golden coins, he changed it for an ordinary goat while the lad slept.

Next morning off went the lad. When he got home, he said to his mother, "What a good fellow the North Wind is! Now he has given me a goat that gives forth golden coins whenever I say, 'Goat, goat, make money!' "

"All very true, I daresay," said his mother. "But I shan't believe it until I see the gold coins made."

"Goat, goat, make money!" said the lad, but the goat didn't.

So the lad went back to the North Wind and got very angry, for he said the goat was worth nothing, and he must have his oatmeal back.

"Well," said the North Wind, "I've nothing else to give you except that old stick in the corner, but it's a stick that if you say, 'Stick, stick, lay on!' lays on until you say, 'Stick, stick, now stop!' "

So, as the way was long, the lad turned in for the night at the same inn. By now he had pretty well guessed what had become of the cloth and the goat, so he lay down on the bed and began to snore, pretending to be asleep.

Now the landlord, who was sure the stick must be worth something, found one just like it. When he heard the lad snore, he was going to exchange the two, but just as he was about to take the stick, the lad yelled out, "Stick, stick, lay on!"

So the stick began to beat the landlord, and the landlord jumped over tables, chairs, and benches, and yelled and roared, "Oh, my! Oh, my! Bid the stick be still, and you shall have both your cloth and your goat!"

So the lad said, "Stick, stick, now stop!"

Then he took the cloth, put it in his pocket, and went home with his stick in his hand, leading the goat by a rope, and so he got his rights for the oatmeal he had lost, and if he didn't live happily ever after, that's not the fault of either you or me.

The Monkeys and the Crocodile

The poem has a good, stirring rhythm and
resembles a humorous ballad. After hearing
the poem read aloud, the children can join
in as you read it to them. You might discuss
teasing—why people tease, etc.

Five little monkeys
  Swinging from a tree;
Teasing Uncle Crocodile,
  Merry as can be.
Swinging high, swinging low,
  Swinging left and right:
"Dear Uncle Crocodile,
  Come and take a bite!"

Five little monkeys
  Swinging in the air;
Heads up, tails up,
  Little do they care.
Swinging up, swinging down,
  Swinging far and near:
"Poor Uncle Crocodile,
  Aren't you hungry, dear?"

Four little monkeys
  Sitting in the tree;
Heads down, tails down,
  Dreary as can be.
Weeping loud, weeping low,
  Crying to each other:
"Wicked Uncle Crocodile,
  To gobble up our brother!"

LAURA E. RICHARDS

All the Way Home

By Lore Segal

Before the story

Ask the children if they remember other
stories concerning journeys (e.g. The
Gingerbread Boy, Hansel and Gretel).
Discuss the reasons why children cry,
and why crying upsets adults.

After the story

The class can build a sequential story
patterned on this one, with each new
character adding to the humour of the tale.
For example, the story could be called
"Room for One More" or "The Bus Ride."
Use experience chart paper, or have each
child create one incident and then join them
all to make a booklet built around the
pattern.

Juliet fell down.
Juliet closed both her eyes and opened
her mouth as wide as she could and
howled.

Her mother kissed her. "Did that make it
better?" the mother asked Juliet.

"Whaaa," answered Juliet, "it's all better
now."

"So what are you crying for?" asked the
mother.

"Because I feel like it," howled Juliet.
"Whaaa!"

"And what are you grinning at, George?"
asked the mother. "Stop it, both of you. All
right then! We're going home this minute!"

"All right," hollered Juliet, "then I'm going
to cry all the way."

So they were walking along, the mother,
and Juliet crying "Whaaa," and George
grinning . . . when they met a dog.

The dog said, "What's the matter with Juliet?
Why is she making so much noise?"

"Dog," said the mother, "I don't know, and
she's going to do it all the way home."

"Well then, I'll tell you what I'll do," said the
dog.

"I'll walk behind Juliet and I'll close both my
eyes and open my snout as wide as I can and
I'll bark all the way home."

So they were walking along, the mother, and
Juliet crying "Whaaa," with George grinning
and the dog barking . . . when they met a cat.

The cat said, "What ever is the matter with
Juliet and that dog? Why are they making such
a lot of noise?"

"Cat," said the mother, "I wish I knew, and
they are going to do it all the way home."

"Then I'll tell you what I'll do," said the cat.
"I'll walk behind the dog and I'll close both my
eyes and open my mouth as wide as I can and
I'll miaow all the way home."

So they were walking along, the mother, and
Juliet crying "Whaaa," with George grinning
and the dog barking and the cat miaowing . . .
when they met a bird.

The bird said, "What on earth is the matter
with Juliet, and the dog and the cat? Why are
they making such a racket?"

"Awful, isn't it?" said the mother.

"I'll tell you what I'll do," said the bird.

"Let me guess," said the mother. "You'll walk
behind the cat and close both your eyes and

44

open your beak as wide as you can and you'll squawk all the way home?"

"Right!" said the bird.

So they were walking along, the mother, and Juliet crying "Whaaa," with George grinning and the dog barking and the cat miaowing and the bird squawking . . . when they came to the house where Juliet lived.

The doorman stood in the door. He shook his head and said, "Uh-uh! You can't come in here, not with all the noise you're making!"

So they had to go on walking, the mother, and Juliet crying "Whaaa," with George grinning and the dog barking and the cat miaowing and the bird squawking, past Juliet's house and up the street and around the corner and around the next corner and the next corner and the next, and when they got back to the house where Juliet lived . . . the doorman stood in the door and shook his head and said, "Uh-uh," so they had to keep walking on, the mother and Juliet and George and the dog and the cat and the bird, crying and grinning and barking and miaowing and squawking.

And as they were turning the corner before the house where Juliet lived, she closed her mouth and opened both her eyes and said, "Mommy, I have to whisper."

Juliet's mother bent her head down. "I don't feel like crying any more. I want to go home," Juliet whispered. Then Juliet's mother whispered in Juliet's ear and in George's ear, and George stopped grinning.

When they got to the house, the doorman quickly opened the door and Juliet and George and the mother ran inside. But the dog and the cat and the bird with their six eyes closed, and one snout, one mouth, and one beak, barking, miaowing, and squawking, walked right past and up the street.

If you see them coming round the corner, tell them to stop making such a racket because Juliet isn't crying any more.

Bedtime

Five minutes, five minutes more, please!
   Let me stay five minutes more!
Can't I just finish the castle
   I'm building here on the floor?
Can't I just finish the story
   I'm reading here in my book?
Can't I just finish this bead-chain—
   It *almost* is finished, look!
Can't I just finish this game, please?
   When a game's once begun
It's a pity never to find out
   Whether you've lost or won.
Can't I just stay five minutes?
   Well, can't I stay just four?
Three minutes, then? two minutes?
   Can't I stay *one* minute more?

ELEANOR FARJEON

How the Little Old Woman Kept Her Geese Warm

By Hope Newell

Before the story

Discuss how people keep warm in the winter (e.g. clothing, homes, blankets, etc.). Ask, "Do animals have difficulty keeping warm in the cold weather?"

After the story

Ask, "Do you think the Little Old Woman made a wise decision switching the two bedrooms? Do you know what a feather bed is? Does anyone sleep with a down-filled quilt? Has anyone ever slept in a sleeping bag? What was it like?"

One cold winter night, the Little Old Woman was out in the barn putting her geese to bed. She gave them some corn and took off their little red coats. Then she brushed each little coat with a whisk-broom and carefully shook out the wrinkles.

As she was folding the coats in a neat pile, she thought: "My poor geese must be very cold at night. I have my cozy fire and my feather bed. But they have not even a blanket to keep them warm."

After the geese had eaten their corn, they began to go to roost.

"Honk, honk!" said the big gander, and he hopped up on the roost.

"Honk, honk!" said the grey goose, and she hopped up on the roost.

"Honk, honk!" said all the other geese, and they hopped up on the roost.

Then the Little Old Woman closed the barn door and went into the house. When she went to bed, she lay awake worrying about the geese. After a while she said to herself: "I cannot sleep a wink for thinking how cold the geese must be. I had better bring them in the house where it is warm."

So the Little Old Woman dressed herself and went out to the barn to fetch the geese. She shooed them off the roost and put on their little red coats. She picked up two geese, and tucking one under each arm, she carried them into the house.

Then she went out to the barn and picked up two more geese. She tucked one goose under each arm and carried them into the house.

When the Little Old Woman had brought all the geese into the house, she said to herself: "Now I must get them ready for bed again." She took off their little red coats and gave the geese some corn. Then she brushed each little coat with a whisk-broom and carefully shook out all the wrinkles.

As she was folding the coats in a neat pile, she thought: "It was very clever of me to bring the geese into the house. Now they will be warm, and I shall be able to sleep."

Then the Little Old Woman undressed herself again and went to bed.

After the geese had eaten their corn, they began to roost.

"Honk, honk!" said the gander, and he hopped up on the foot of the Little Old Woman's bed.

"Honk, honk!" said the grey goose, and she

hopped up on the foot of the Little Old Woman's bed.

"Honk, honk!" said all the other geese, and they tried to hop up on the foot of the Little Old Woman's bed.

But it was not a very big bed, and there was not enough room for all the geese to roost. They began to fight. They pushed and shoved each other. They hissed and squawked and flapped their wings.

All night long the geese pushed and shoved each other. All night long they hissed and squawked and flapped their wings.

They made so much noise that the Little Old Woman did not sleep a wink.

"This will never do," she said. "When they were in the barn, I did not sleep for thinking how cold they must be. When they are in the house, I cannot sleep because they make so much noise. Perhaps if I use my head, I shall know what to do."

The Little Old Woman tied a wet towel around her forehead. Then she sat down with her forefinger against her nose and shut her eyes.

She used her head and used her head, and after a while she knew what to do.

"I will move the roost into the house," she said. "The geese will have the cozy fire to keep them warm. Then I will move my bed out into the barn. My feather bed will keep me warm, and I will not be worrying about the geese. They will not keep me awake with their noise. I shall sleep very comfortably in the barn."

The Little Old Woman moved the roost into the house, and she moved her bed out into the barn.

When night came again, she brought the geese into the house. After she had fed them some corn, she took off their little red coats. Then they all hopped up on the roost, and the Little Old Woman went out to the barn to sleep.

Her feather bed kept her as warm as toast. She was not worried about the geese, because she knew that they were warm too. So she slept as sound as a top all night long.

Conversation

Read the poem to the children, using
different voices to indicate the two
characters. Ask the children, "Who could
be asking to get into the mouse's house?"
Put the story on chart paper, and have
volunteers read the responses to your
questions as the cat who wants to trick the
mouse into letting him in. If the children
are able, you can continue the conversation
as the cat through improvisation (e.g. "I
wonder if you could help me. I'm lost and I
hoped you could show me the way to the
store"); the children will then answer as
mice.

"Mousie, mousie,
   Where is your little wee housie?"
      "Here is the door,
      Under the floor,"
         Said mousie, mousie.

"Mousie, mousie,
   May I come into your housie?"
      "You can't get in,
      You have to be thin,"
         Said mousie, mousie.

"Mousie, mousie,
   Won't you come out of your housie?"
      "I'm sorry to say,
      I'm busy all day,"
         Said mousie, mousie.

ROSE FYLEMAN

Big Sister and Little Sister

By Charlotte Zolotow

Before the story

Have the children complete a chart story
that begins:
I like to be alone

when_____

when_____

After the story

Ask, "Why did Little Sister hide from Big
Sister? Why did she suddenly tell Big Sister
where she had been hiding?"

Can any children remember a time when
a big brother or sister helped them out of
a difficult situation?

Once there was a big sister and a little
sister.

The big sister always took care. Even
when she was skipping, she took care that her
little sister stayed on the path.

When she rode her bicycle, she gave her little
sister a ride.

When she was walking to school, she took
the little sister's hand and helped her cross the
road. When they were playing in the fields,
she made sure little sister didn't get lost. When
they were sewing, she made sure little sister's
needle was threaded and that little sister held
the scissors the right way.

Big sister took care of everything, and little
sister thought there was nothing big sister
couldn't do.

Little sister would sometimes cry, but big
sister always made her stop. First she'd put her
arm around her, then she'd hold out her handkerchief and say, "Here, blow."

Big sister knew everything. "Don't do it like
that," she'd say. "Do it this way." And little
sister did. Nothing could bother big sister. She
knew too much.

But one day little sister wanted to be alone.
She was tired of big sister saying, "Sit here."
"Go there." "Do it this way." "Come along."
And while big sister was getting lemonade and
biscuits for them, little sister slipped away,
out of the house, out of the garden, down the
road, and into the meadow where daisies and
grass hid her.

Very soon she heard big sister calling, calling,
and calling her. But she didn't answer. She
heard big sister's voice getting louder when she
was closer, and fainter when she went the other
way, calling, calling.

Little sister leaned back in the daisies. She
thought about lemonade and biscuits. She
thought about the book big sister had promised
to read to her. She thought about big sister
saying, "Sit here." "Go there." "Do it this way."
"Come along." No one told little sister anything
now.

The daisies bent back and forth in the sun. A
big bee bumbled by. The weeds scratched under
her bare legs. But she didn't move. She heard
big sister's voice coming back. It came closer
and closer and closer. And suddenly big sister
was so near little sister could have touched her.

Big sister sat down in the daisies. She stopped
calling. And she began to cry. She cried and
cried just the way little sister often did.

When the little sister cried, the big one
comforted her. But there was no one to put an
arm around big sister. No one took out a
handkerchief and said, "Here, blow." Big sister
just sat there crying alone.

Little sister stood up but big sister didn't
even see her, she was crying so much. Little
sister went over and put her arm around big
sister. She took out her handkerchief and said
kindly, "Here, blow."

Big sister did. Then the little sister hugged
her.

"Where have you been?" big sister asked.

"Never mind," said little sister.

"Let's go home and have some lemonade."

And from that day on little sister and big
sister both took care of each other because little
sister had learned from big sister and now they
both knew how.

50

Me and My Giant

Have a discussion with the children about
giants they are familiar with in stories,
films, and on television.

Read the poem to the children twice.
Ask, "How did the person in the poem
communicate with giants? Why didn't they
talk to each other? If you had a giant for
a friend, what could he do for you? What
could you do for him?"

I have a friend who is a giant,
And he lives where the tall weeds grow.
He's high as a mountain and wide as a
    barn
And I only come up to his toe, you know,
  I only come up to his toe.

When the daylight grows dim I talk with
    him
Way down in the marshy sands,
And his ear is too far away to hear,
But still he understands, he 'stands,
  I know he understands.

For we have a code called the "scratch-
    tap code,"
And here is what we do—
I scratch his toe . . . once means, "Hello"
And twice means, "How are you?"
Three means, "Does it look like rain?"
Four times means, "Don't cry."
Five times means, "I'll scratch you a
    joke."
And six times means, "Goodbye,"
    "Goodbye,"
  Six times means, "Goodbye."

And he answers me by tapping his toe—
Once means, "Hello, friend."
Two taps means, "It's very nice
    to feel your scratch again."

Three taps means, "It's lonely here
    with my head in the top of the sky."
Four taps means, "Today an eagle
    smiled as she flew by."
Five taps means, "Oops, I just bumped
    my head against the moon."
Six means, "Sigh" and seven means,
    "Bye"
And eight means, "Come back soon,
    soon, soon."
  Eight means, "Come back soon."

And then I scratch a thousand times,
And he taps with a bappity-bimm,
And he laughs so hard he shakes the
    sky—
  That means I'm tickling him!

SHEL SILVERSTEIN

Rumpelstiltskin

By The Brothers Grimm

Before the story

Ask the children several riddles:
1. I wag my tail. I bark. What am I?
2. Birds live in me. I give you shade in the summer. What am I?
3. I ride on a big red truck. Fighting fires is my job. Who am I?

Introduce "Rumpelstiltskin" by explaining that there is a strange riddle in the story that will change the life of the miller's daughter.

After the story

The children can dramatize this story with simple handpuppets. They may work with partners, one playing the daughter and one playing Rumpelstiltskin, to improvise the dialogue.

or

The children may create Rumpelstiltskin puppets, and one by one role-play the story, with your puppet as the miller's daughter.

There was once a miller who was poor, but he had one beautiful daughter. It happened one day that he came to speak with the king, and to give himself importance, he told him that he had a daughter who could spin gold out of straw. The king said to the miller,

"That is an art that pleases me well; if your daughter is as clever as you say, bring her to my castle tomorrow, that I may put her to the test."

When the girl was brought to him, he led her into a room that was quite full of straw, and gave her a wheel and spindle, and said, "Now set to work, and if by the early morning you have not spun this straw to gold you shall die." And he shut the door himself, and left her there alone.

And so the poor miller's daughter was left there sitting, and could not think what to do for her life; she had no notion how to set to work to spin gold from straw, and her distress grew so great that she began to weep. Then all at once the door opened, and in came a little man, who said,

"Good evening, miller's daughter; why are you crying?"

"Oh!" answered the girl, "I have got to spin gold out of straw, and I don't understand the business."

Then the little man said, "What will you give me if I spin it for you?"

"My necklace," said the girl.

The little man took the necklace, seated himself before the wheel, and whirr, whirr, whirr! three times round and the bobbin was full; then he took up another, and whirr, whirr, whirr! three times round, and that was full; and so he went on till the morning, when all the straw had been spun, and all the bobbins were full of gold. At sunrise came the king, and when he saw the gold he was astonished and very much rejoiced, for he was very avaricious. He had the miller's daughter taken into another room filled with straw, much bigger than the last, and told her that as she valued her life she must spin it all in one night. The girl did not know what to do, so she began to cry, and then the door opened, and the little man appeared and said,

"What will you give me if I spin all this straw into gold?"

"The ring from my finger," answered the girl.

So the little man took the ring, and began again to send the wheel whirring round, and by the next morning all the straw was spun into glistening gold. The king was rejoiced beyond measure at the sight, but as he could never have enough of gold, he had the miller's daughter taken into a still larger room full of straw, and said,

"This, too, must be spun in one night, and if you accomplish it you shall be my wife." For he thought, "Although she is but a miller's daughter, I am not likely to find any one richer in the whole world."

As soon as the girl was left alone, the little man appeared for the third time and said, "What will you give me if I spin the straw for you this time?"

"I have nothing left to give," answered the girl.

"Then you must promise me the first child you have after you are queen," said the little man.

"But who knows whether that will happen?" thought the girl; but as she did not know what else to do in her necessity, she promised the little man what he desired, upon which he began to spin, until all the straw was gold. And when in the morning the king came and found all done according to his wish, he caused the wedding to be held at once, and the miller's pretty daughter became a queen.

In a year's time she brought a fine child into the world, and thought no more of the little man; but one day he came suddenly into her room, and said, "Now give me what you promised me."

The queen was terrified greatly, and offered the little man all the riches of the kingdom if he would only leave the child; but the little man said, "No, I would rather have something living than all the treasures of the world."

Then the queen began to lament and to weep, so that the little man had pity upon her.

"I will give you three days," said he, "and if at the end of that time you cannot tell my name, you must give up the child to me."

Then the queen spent the whole night in thinking over all the names that she had ever heard, and sent a messenger through the land to ask far and wide for all the names that could be found. And when the little man came next day (beginning with Caspar, Melchior, Balthazar), she repeated all she knew, and went through the whole list, but after each the little man said,

"That is not my name."

The second day the queen sent to inquire of all the neighbours what the servants were called, and told the little man all the most unusual and singular names, saying, "Perhaps you are called Roast-ribs, or Sheep-shanks, or Spindleshanks?"

But he answered nothing but "That is not my name."

The third day the messenger came back again, and said, "I have not been able to find one single new name; but as I passed through the woods I came to a high hill, and near it was a little house, and before the house burned a fire, and round the fire danced a comical little man, and he hopped on one leg and cried,

> "To-day do I bake, to-morrow I brew,
> The day after that the queen's child
>   comes in;
> And oh! I am glad that nobody knew
> That the name I am called is
>   Rumpelstiltskin!"

You cannot think how pleased the queen was to hear that name, and soon afterwards, when the little man walked in and said, "Now, Mrs. Queen, what is my name?" she said at first,

"Are you called Jack?"

"No," he answered.

"Are you called Harry?" she asked again.

"No," answered he. And then she said,

"Then perhaps your name is Rumpelstilt-skin!"

"Who told you that? Who told you that?" cried the little man, and in his anger he stamped with his right foot so hard that it went into the ground above his knee; then he seized his left foot with both his hands in such a fury that he split in two, and there was an end of him.

Puppy and I

I met a man as I went walking;
We got talking,
Man and I.
"Where are you going to, Man?" I said
  (I said to the Man as he went by).
"Down to the village, to get some bread.
  Will you come with me?" "No, not I."

I met a Horse as I went walking;
We got talking,
Horse and I.
"Where are you going to, Horse, to-
  day?"
  (I said to the Horse as he went by).
"Down to the village to get some hay.
  Will you come with me?" "No, not I."

I met a Woman as I went walking;
We got talking,
Woman and I.
"Where are you going to, Woman, so
  early?"
  (I said to the Woman as she went by).
"Down to the village to get some barley.
  Will you come with me?" "No, not I."

I met some Rabbits as I went walking;
We got talking,
Rabbits and I.
"Where are you going in your brown fur
  coats?"
  (I said to the Rabbits as they went
  by).
"Down to the village to get some oats.
  Will you come with us?" "No, not I."

I met a Puppy as I went walking;
We got talking,
Puppy and I.
"Where are you going this nice fine
  day?"
  (I said to the Puppy as he went by).
"Up in the hills to roll and play."
  "*I'll* come with you, Puppy," said I.

A.A. MILNE

Mrs. Beggs and the Wizard

BY MERCER MAYER

Before the story

Discuss the concept of a boarding house:
people live there but not in families;
someone must own the house and look after
it; people come and go all the time.

After the story

Ask the children to describe the strange
events that were going on in Mrs. Beggs's
boarding house. Ask who they think the
new visitor at the door will be at the end of
the story.

One day a stranger appeared at Mrs. Beggs's boarding house looking for a room to rent. His calling card read

Z.P. ALABASIUM
Wizard Extraordinaire.

"This room suits me fine," he said. "I'll take it." He gave Mrs. Beggs a month's deposit and she gave him the key.

That evening Mr. Alabasium didn't show up for dinner, so Mrs. Beggs fixed him a tray of food and took it up to his room.

"Just leave it on the floor, Mrs. Beggs," he said, not bothering to open the door.

"Dear me," she said and went down the stairs.

That night as she lay in bed, she heard strange noises from the room above. Up the stairs crept Mrs. Beggs, followed closely by all the guests who had also heard the noises.

"Oh my, what can be happening?" she said, knocking on Mr. Alabasium's door.

"Nothing to concern yourself with, Mrs. Beggs," said Mr. Alabasium. "Now leave me be." With that he slammed the door shut.

That would have suited Mrs. Beggs just fine, for she wasn't a particularly nosey person.

However, the next morning she found the fresh cut flowers on the dining room table

withered and dead. "Oh well, I'll cut some more," she thought, and went outside.

In the backyard, her beautiful garden was overgrown with weeds, thistles, and briars. To make matters worse, the birdbath was full of toads.

As if that wasn't enough, a giant windstorm came up that afternoon just as Mrs. Beggs was hanging out the laundry. With a swoosh and a swirl, Mrs. Beggs and the fresh clean laundry were blown all over the yard.

But even stranger things were yet to happen.

The following day a rainstorm thundered through the parlour, soaking everyone to the bone.

"Oh I'm so sorry," cried Mrs. Beggs. "It has never rained in here before."

At lunch the tables and chairs floated through the air. The dishes and fine china fell off the shelves.

Old man Blagget's wheelchair flew out the front door, carrying poor old man Blagget far across town.

Grannie Appleton's cane turned into a snake and slithered away. Of course Grannie Appleton screamed.

Strange things wandered through the house or just floated through the air, frightening the guests.

Mr. Plimp's beaver hat turned back into a

55

beaver and bit Mr. Plimp on the nose.

Mrs. Fizzle found reptiles in her bed and fainted. Needless to say, the guests were very unhappy and complained.

To make matters even worse, a blizzard raged into the house, howling and blowing snow everywhere. "Mrs. Beggs," said Major Clearlob, "I believe I can speak for the rest of the guests. That Mr. Alabasium is up to no good. Either he goes or we go."

"Oh dear," thought Mrs. Beggs. "This is becoming very bad for business. I must find out if Mr. Alabasium is up to no good or not."

"Mr. Alabasium," she said knocking on his door, "I was wondering if . . ." But before she finished talking she found herself dressed in a ballet costume, standing on a giant turtle. "Oh dear," she said. "This must stop." So she called the constable.

The constable came and knocked on the door. "Open up, this is the constable."

Suddenly the constable turned into a ram. "*Baaaaaaaaa,*" he said and ran down the stairs.

"That does it," Mrs. Beggs said angrily. She went to her closet. She opened the door. Reaching high up in the closet, she pulled down an old tattered box from the top shelf.

"This may not be the right thing to do," she thought, "but one must do something." The top of the box read

WITCHERY FOR FUN AND PROFIT.

It had belonged to her great aunt Celia, who flew away on a vacuum cleaner one day—not having any broomsticks on hand—and was never seen again.

Mrs. Beggs put on the costume, which was a little too large, and sat down to read the instruction booklet.

"There," she said. "I hope this will do the trick." Then she chanted, ever so quietly,

> "*I've had blizzards,*
> *Snakes and lizards.*
> *I've had rain and wind to bear.*"

As she spoke, the room filled with smoke.

> "*I've heard noise and lots of howling,*
> *Tables floating through the air.*"

Bats darted through the room and strange things peered from the dark.

> "*Powers creeping, I command you.*
> *Get that wizard out of here!*"

With a howl the roomful of strange things dashed through the window and were gone. Putting everything neatly away, Mrs. Beggs went to bed.

Later that evening Mr. Alabasium slept well. The window to his room slid slowly open. Quietly, ever so quietly, in crept a group of very strange things. They tied him up with a wizard-proof rope. They tickled his toes and tweaked his nose. They carried him quietly out of the house and through the back streets of the town. They left Z.P. ALABASIUM, *Wizard Extraordinaire*, at the city dump and flew off in the night.

The next day, when nothing strange happened at the boarding house, the guests were overjoyed.

"My, my, it's so very peaceful around here," commented Mrs. Fizzle.

"It most certainly is," replied the other guests, smiling their approval.

By late afternoon, Mr. Clearlob sighed and said, "It's far too peaceful around here. I'm bored to tears."

"So are we," the others replied.

At dinnertime, everyone quietly sipped their soup. Then the doorbell rang.

"I wonder who that could be at this hour," said Mrs. Beggs, and she went to answer the door.

Beware of Me!

Read the poem aloud to the children in a
strong, powerful voice, changing the role in
the last verse to someone who is afraid.
Ask the children, "What things scare you?"

i stand on the rock
ho, bear!
beware of me!

i stand on the tree
ho, eagle!
beware of me!

i stand on the mountain
ho, enemy!
beware of me!

i stand in the camp
ho, chiefs!
beware of me!

here comes a bee!
i run and hide!
he would sting me!

CHEROKEE INDIAN

The Three Billy Goats Gruff

BY PETER CHRISTIAN ASBJÖRNSEN AND JÖRGEN MOE

Before the story

Ask the children, "If you had to cross a bridge, and if there was a scary creature living under the bridge, how could you get rid of the creature?"

During the story

The children can join in on the refrain: Trip, trap! Trip, trap! Trip, trap!

O nce on a time there were three Billy Goats who were to go up to the hillside to make themselves fat, and the name of all three was "Gruff."

On the way up was a bridge over a stream they had to cross; and under the bridge lived a great ugly Troll, with eyes as big as saucers and a nose as long as a poker.

So first of all came the youngest Billy Goat Gruff to cross the bridge.

"*Trip, trap! Trip, trap!*" went the bridge.

"WHO'S THAT tripping over my bridge?" roared the Troll.

"Oh! it is only I, the tiniest Billy Goat Gruff; and I'm going up to the hillside to make myself fat," said the Billy Goat, with such a small voice.

"Now, I'm coming to gobble you up," said the Troll.

"Oh, no! pray don't take me. I'm too little, that I am," said the Billy Goat. "Wait a bit till the second Billy Goat Gruff comes; he's much bigger."

"Well! be off with you," said the Troll.

A little while after, came the second Billy Goat Gruff to cross the bridge.

"*Trip, trap! Trip, trap! Trip, trap!*" went the bridge.

"WHO'S THAT tripping over my bridge?" roared the Troll.

"Oh! it's the second Billy Goat Gruff, and I'm going up to the hillside to make myself fat," said the Billy Goat, who hadn't such a small voice.

After the story

Have the children retell the story. As you narrate it, they can answer the question in "Before the story," role-playing the first, second, and third Billy Goats Gruff.

"Now, I'm coming to gobble you up," said the Troll.

"Oh, no! don't take me. Wait a little till the big Billy Goat Gruff comes; he's much bigger."

"Very well! be off with you," said the Troll.

But just then up came the big Billy Goat Gruff.

"TRIP, TRAP! TRIP, TRAP! TRIP, TRAP! TRIP, TRAP!" went the bridge, for the Billy Goat was so heavy that the bridge creaked and groaned under him.

"WHO'S THAT tramping over my bridge?" roared the Troll.

"IT'S I! THE BIG BILLY GOAT GRUFF," said the Billy Goat, who had an ugly hoarse voice of his own.

"Now, I'm coming to gobble you up," roared the Troll.

"Well, come along! I've got two spears, to fight you with;

    I've got besides two curling-stones,
    And I'll crush you to bits, body and
       bones."

That was what the big Billy Goat said; and so he flew at the Troll, and poked him and knocked him, and crushed him to bits, body and bones, and tossed him out into the burn, and after that he went up to the hillside. There the Billy Goats got so fat that they were scarce able to walk home again; and if the fat hasn't fallen off them, why they're still fat; and so—

    "Snip, snap, snout,
    This tale's told out."

Open the Door

This charming poem contains a basic refrain
pattern that allows the children to be part
of the reading experience. As you reread,
encourage them to participate in part of the
chorus. For example:

"Who do you see?
Who do you see?"

Different groups could paint the various
characters and place them behind a large,
cut-out door.

Open the door and who'll come in?
  Who'll come in?
  Who'll come in?
Open the door and who'll come in,
  So early Monday morning?

My little pussycat, she'll come in.
Rubbing her fur against my shin.
She'll arch her back and she'll step right
    in,
  So early Monday morning.

Open the door and who'll come in?
  Who'll come in?
  Who'll come in?
Open the door and who'll come in,
  So early Tuesday morning?

My little puppy dog, he'll come in,
Mud on his paws and mud on his chin.
He'll bounce and he'll pounce as he
    dashes in,
  So early Tuesday morning.

Open the door and who'll come in?
  Who'll come in?
  Who'll come in?
Open the door and who'll come in,
  So early Wednesday morning?

My little Dicky bird, he'll come in,
His eyes so black and his legs so thin.
He'll fly to his cage and he'll pop right in,
  So early Wednesday morning.

Open the door and who do you see?
  Who do you see?
  Who do you see?
Open the door and who do you see,
  So early Thursday morning?

Beulah the pony is visiting me,
Nuzzling her nose against my knee,
Asking for sugar, as plain as can be,
  So early Thursday morning.

Open the door and who'll be there?
  Who'll be there?
  Who'll be there?
Open the door and who'll be there,
  So early Friday morning?

The Skillipot turtles, a tiny pair,
Their shells so hard and their heads so
    bare.
It takes them an hour to get anywhere
  So early Friday morning.

Open the door and what do you know?
  What do you know?
  What do you know?
Open the door and what do you know,
  So early Saturday morning?

My beautiful bunnies are white as snow,
And their pink little noses wiggle so.
Three pretty hops, and in they go,
  So early Saturday morning.

MARION EDEY AND DOROTHY GRIDER

Half-a-Ball-of-Kenki

RETOLD BY VERNA AARDEMA

Before the story

Ask the children if they have stuffed animals in their homes. Ask them why they enjoy such toys, and why stories often have animals in them that talk.

During the story

Read the sound words with vigour, repeating them as often as necessary, having the children join in when they can.

After the story

Ask the children to recall interesting words they remember from the story. Put these words on cards for the children to say aloud and enjoy.

kye, kye, kye
gben, gben, gben
kuputu, kuputu, kuputu
pamdal, pamdal
tih, tih
kpong, kpong, kpong
pip, pip, pip
tuk-pik, tuk-pik
kpung, kpung, kpung

Long ago and far away, fly and leopard were friends. One day Leopard said, "Fly, let's go looking for girls to marry."

"Yo!" cried Fly. "That will be fun for me. The girls will like me better than you."

"*Kye, kye, kye,*" laughed Leopard. "We shall see!" Then he bathed and oiled his fur. And he put a gold chain around his neck, and anklets with bells of gold on his front feet. To make sure his friend did not outshine him, he tied up his dirty old sleeping mat and gave it to Fly to carry on his head.

The two set out down the path, the gold bells singing *gben, gben, gben* as they walked along.

Presently, they came to a village. Fly entered first. He put down his burden and said to the people in the plaza, "Mothers all and fathers all, I give you morning greetings."

The people greeted him in return, and the young maids gathered about him.

Then Leopard swaggered through the gate, jingling his anklets with every step *gben, gben, gben*! He smiled a crafty smile and said, "Mothers all and fathers all . . ."

But the chief cried, "Off with you! How dare you enter our village!" He said, "*Sah!*" to his dog. And the dog bolted after Leopard. Leopard went flying *kuputu, kuputu, kuputu* out the gate!

Fly followed him out. And the two went on. At length, they arrived at another town.

Again, Fly entered first. The people greeted him, and the young girls clustered around him.

But when Leopard arrived, he was driven off just as before.

Back on the path Leopard said, "Look here, Fly! Give me that old mat. And you take these gold things and adorn yourself. If it is because of that mat that the girls love you, we shall see!"

So Fly put on the gold ornaments, Leopard carried the mat, and they went on their way.

When they reached the next village, Leopard entered first, with the dirty old mat on his head. He said, "Mothers all and fathers all, I give you midday greetings."

But the women and children screamed and ran *pamdal* into their houses. And the men grabbed their spears! Leopard scuttled away so fast that the mat fell off his head.

A small time later Leopard watched through a crack in the fence as Fly entered the plaza and was welcomed by the people. Leopard heard a maiden say, "*Tih, tih!* How handsome you look with those gold things on. If it were not for the beating I would get, I would go away with you."

Leopard turned away in disgust.

60

He said, "When the moon is out, the stars are dim. And I can't go looking for girls with a handsome man like him!"

When Fly joined Leopard on the path, Leopard was overcome with jealousy. He cried, "Stand still, Fly! Take off those gold things and give them to me, quickly, quickly, quickly!"

As Fly was slipping them off, Leopard plucked a long creeper. He grabbed hold of Fly and bound him to a palm tree—winding the creeper *kpong, kpong, kpong*. Then he hid himself nearby.

Presently, Nkatee, the Peanut, came down the path on her way to market. She was stepping daintily *pip, pip, pip* over the roots that crisscrossed the path. She saw the bundle on the tree and asked, "Who is hanging there so very black? Who is hanging there so very glossy?"

Fly sang:

"It's I, the Fly, tied
By Leopard to this tree,
Because the girls hated him,
But they loved me.
Ooo! Please come and set me free!"

But Nkatee said, "If I set you free, Leopard will make peanut soup of me!" And she hurried off *pip-pip-pip-pip, pip-pip-pip*!

Soon Kwadu, the Banana, came striding by *tuk-pik, tuk-pik*. She saw Fly and asked, "Who is hanging there so very black? Who is hanging there so very glossy?"

Fly sang:

"It's I, the Fly, tied
By Leopard to this tree,
Because the girls hated him,
But they loved me.
Ooo! Please come and set me free!"

Kwadu said, "If I loosened you, Leopard would mash me to fu-fu!" (Fu-fu is mashed banana.) And she hurried off *tuk-pik, tuk-pik, tuk-pik*!

At last there came along Dokonfa, half a ball of kenki, which is cold cornmeal mush. Half-a-Ball-of-Kenki was singing:

"I'm Half-a-Ball-of-Kenki,
Which is better than none.
I'm Half-a-Ball-of-Kenki,
And two of me makes one."

Then she saw Fly and asked, "Who is hanging there so very black? Who is hanging there so very glossy?"

Fly sang:

"It's I, the Fly, tied
By Leopard to this tree,
Because the girls hated him,
But they loved me.
Ooo! Please come and set me free!"

Half-a-Ball-of-Kenki said, "I have heard you. And I shall set you free!" She unwound the creeper *kpung, kpung, kpung*.

And Fly flew off *wurrrr!*

Then Leopard leaped *harrr* out of the bushes! He bellowed, "Why have you freed my man?"

"Well, I have done it," said Half-a-Ball-of-Kenki. "And what you will do to me do!"

"You and I will fight," said Leopard.

Half-a-Ball-of-Kenki said, "It is already early evening. If we are going to fight, let us make a fire first." So they broke wood and set it alight in the middle of the path.

Then they began to wrestle. Round and round they tumbled. And soon Leopard tore Half-a-Ball-of-Kenki from him and threw her *blim* against a tree!

"A thing like that is nothing," said Half-a-Ball-of Kenki as she pulled herself together.

They fought again. And Leopard slammed Half-a-Ball-of-Kenki deep into the sand! *Ras, ras, ras* she dug herself out, and brushed herself off. Then she said, "Now, we'll really fight! That was just for practice."

They grappled again, rolling on the ground *dadwa, dadwa, dadwa*. Then suddenly Half-a-Ball-of-Kenki gathered all her strength, tied up leopard, and threw him *Kabat* into the fire!

"I'm out! I'm out! I'm out!" cried Leopard.

And that is how the leopard got his cry.

When he came out of the fire, his body was all spotted. There were black spots where the charred wood had touched him. There were white spots where the ashes had touched him. And that is how the leopard got a spotted coat.

And to this day flies sit upon the leaves in which kenki has been wrapped. And people say that they are saying thank you because of what Half-a-Ball-of-Kenki did for Fly long ago.

The Mysterious Cat

This is a soft poem that evokes the feeling
of the world of cats for the children. When
you read it aloud, try to create an image
of a mysterious feline in the room.

Ask the children, "What stories about
cats do you know? What colours and kinds
of cats have you known?"

I saw a proud, mysterious cat,
I saw a proud, mysterious cat,
Too proud to catch a mouse or rat—
Mew, mew, mew.

But catnip she would eat, and purr,
But catnip she would eat, and purr.
And goldfish she did much prefer—
Mew, mew, mew. . . .

Did you ever hear of a thing like that?
Did you ever hear of a thing like that?
Did you ever hear of a thing like that?
Oh, what a proud mysterious cat.
Oh, what a proud mysterious cat.
Oh, what a proud mysterious cat.
Mew . . . Mew . . . Mew.

VACHEL LINDSAY

The Bunyip of Berkeley's Creek

By Jenny Wagner

Before the story

Tell the class they are going to hear a story about an imaginary animal from Australia. Do they know any other animals from "Down Under"? (e.g. the kangaroo)

After the story

The children can create the Bunyip as a class, individually or with a partner. Torn paper could be used, or moveable parts that are clipped together to form the body.

Late one night, for no particular reason, something stirred in the black mud at the bottom of Berkeley's Creek. The fish swam away in fright, and the night birds in the trees hid their heads under their wings.

When they looked again, something very large and very muddy was sitting on the bank.

"What am I?" it murmured. "What am I, what am I, what am I?"

And the night birds quickly hid their heads under their wings again.

In the morning the thing was still sitting there, scraping the mud off itself to see what was underneath. "What am I?" it kept saying. "What am I?"

But the night birds were all asleep.

A passing platypus solved the problem. "You are a bunyip," he said.

"Bunyip," murmured the bunyip contentedly. "Bunyip." Then he sat up straight and called out, "What do I look like?"

But the platypus had dived into the creek.

"Am I handsome?" called the bunyip. "Am I?"

But nobody answered him, and the bunyip went on sitting there for a long time, lost in thought.

Presently a wallaby came by to drink at the creek.

"What do bunyips look like?" asked the bunyip.

"Horrible," said the wallaby. "They have webbed feet, and feathers."

"Fine, handsome feathers," said the bunyip hopefully.

"Horrible feathers," said the wallaby firmly, and finished his drink and hopped off.

"Handsome webbed feet?" called the bunyip, but there was no answer. The bunyip sighed and walked off to find someone else.

There was a rustling in the bushes behind him, and suddenly an emu shot past.

"Wait!" called the bunyip, running after him. "What do bunyips look like?"

The emu stopped and considered. "They have fur," he said at last, "and tails."

"How many tails?" asked the bunyip.

"One to each bunyip," replied the emu.

"Fine, handsome tails," said the bunyip.

"Horrible tails," said the emu. "And even more horrible fur." And he settled his feathers and crouched down low, and streaked off into the distance.

The bunyip wandered sadly along the creek. "Will someone tell me what bunyips look like?" he said, to anyone who would listen.

But there was no answer.

Further along the creek he met a man. The man was busy with a notebook and pencil, and did not look at the bunyip.

"Sh," he said, "I'm busy."

The bunyip waited for a long time, and then he said, very slowly and clearly, "Can you

63

please tell me what bunyips look like?"

"Yes," said the man, without looking up. "Bunyips don't look like anything."

"Like nothing?" said the bunyip.

"Like nothing at all," said the man.

"Are you sure?" said the bunyip.

"Quite sure," said the man, and looked right through him. "Bunyips simply don't exist."

The bunyip was shaken. Then he sighed a long, deep sigh. "What a pity," he murmured. "What a pity, what a pity." And he walked slowly back to his waterhole. Then he fished his belongings out of the water, packed them in his bunyip bag, and walked away. No one saw him go.

The bunyip walked all day, and just as the sun was setting he came to a quiet, still billabong.

"This will do," said the bunyip to himself.

"No one can see me here. I can be as handsome as I like." And he unpacked his bag, and laid his bunyip comb and mirror out on the sand, and put his billy on to boil.

No one saw him and no one spoke to him.

But late that night, for no particular reason, something stirred in the black mud at the bottom of the billabong. The bunyip put his comb down in surprise, and stared. Something very large and very muddy was sitting on the bank.

"What am I?" it murmured. "What am I, what am I?"

The bunyip jumped up in delight. "You are a bunyip!" he shouted.

"Am I? Am I really?" asked the other bunyip; and then, "What do I look like?"

"You look just like me," said the bunyip happily. And he lent her his mirror to prove it.

Good Morning

This gentle poem to morning will help the
children to pattern their own good mornings
as a class on chart paper. For example:
>Good morning to our pets.
>Good morning to the sun.
>Good morning to the teacher.

Good morning to the great trees
That bend above this little house;
Good morning to the wind that comes
And goes among the leaves, and sings;
Good morning to the birds, the grass,
Good morning to the bare ground;
Good morning, pond across the way
That must have opened both its eyes;
Good morning, everything that shines
Or doesn't shine; good morning, mole
And worm and nesting mouse—good
    morning,
Morning to all things that ever
Were and will be, and that are.

MARK VAN DOREN

The King's Monster

By Carolyn Haywood

Before the story

What stories about strange creatures do
the children know? (Refer back to "Who's
in Rabbit's House?") Why do writers create
stories about monsters for children to read?

After the story

Discuss the King's reasons for not wanting
his daughter married. Ask the children
what they thought the monster might have
looked like before they knew it was a field
mouse.

Everyone knew about the king's monster. Everyone had talked about it for years. Old women, gossiping over their teacups, said to each other, "The king's monster must be a terrible thing." Young women in the marketplace shook their heads. "It's a man-eating monster." Many believed that the king's servants, armed with great nets, caught naughty boys and fed them to it. Although no one knew of any boy who had wound up as the monster's supper, nevertheless children were warned not to go near the castle and naughty little boys were rebuked with the warning, "Do you want the king's monster to eat you?"

There was much speculation as to the appearance of the monster. "Is it hairy?" "Is it scaly?" "Does it have horns?" Dick Blabbermouth said he had seen the monster, but no one believed anything Dick Blabbermouth said.

"It's a disgrace!" the barber said over every head he cut and face he shaved. "I see no reason why the king should keep such a beast." The customers all agreed.

It was rumoured that the monster was shut up in the dungeon of the castle, but the king's nearest neighbours said, "Not so! The monster must be kept outdoors somewhere. Its odour is polluting the atmosphere and making our air unfit to breathe."

"True," said another neighbour, "and wherever the monster is housed, the roaring in the night keeps my whole family awake."

Only one was unsure of the monster's whereabouts. "It's strange, but my brother-in-law, who is a footman to the king, says he hears nothing."

"Your brother-in-law," cried the man's wife, "is as deaf as a post. Naturally he can't hear the monster. But surely he can smell the stench."

"He says it comes from the garbage that the cook throws into the moat," said her husband.

"Bah!" cried his wife.

The rest of the neighbours nodded their heads. "It's the king's monster that we hear and smell."

Letters of complaint, like snowstorms, arrived at the castle. When they were read to the king, he threw back his head and laughed. "What a monster!" he would cry. "What a monster I have!"

The Princess Gabriella, the king's only child, had heard her father tell about his monster when she was a little girl, curled up on the queen's throne beside her father's. Otherwise, the throne was empty, for the queen had died shortly after the birth of the princess.

The princess never asked the king where the monster was kept. She was afraid he would tell her, and she really didn't want to know.

When the princess grew up, she almost forgot about the monster, for now she had balls and beautiful clothes to think about. But the king's subjects continued to talk about the terrible beast, and travellers carried news of it across the borders into neighbouring kingdoms. The monster became very famous, and the thought of it filled people with fear.

Now every year the king had a great festival to celebrate the princess's birthday. It was a day of revels and much buffoonery. The princess was carried on a litter through the streets, past the king's cheering subjects. The biggest event was the jousting tournament, held in the courtyard of the castle. Princes, earls, and knights came from neighbouring kingdoms to participate in the tournament. The princess was always present, and each year from the time she was a little girl she had eyes only for Prince Michael. He was always the victor, always unseating his opponent. It was observed by many that Prince Michael's eyes rested on the princess with longing.

By the time the princess reached the age of sixteen, her beauty and charm were known beyond the borders of her father's kingdom. Soon suitors for her hand began to arrive, bearing gifts.

They came on horseback, in sedan chairs, and in sumptuous coaches. So many appeared that the king had to post a sign. "Suitors for the hand of the princess, please use the postern door. Wipe your feet!"

Hopeful suitors presented themselves to the king. They told him of their love for the princess, of the precious jewels they would give her, of their wealth in both land and gold.

The king listened to each one, and to each he said, "Only a brave and courageous man shall wed my daughter. Only one who can wrestle and overcome my monster can present his suit to the princess. Are you willing to fight the king's monster?"

Now they all had heard of the terrible monster, and one by one they fled from the presence of the king. He had set the price too high.

Before long the king was convinced that he would never have to give his daughter in marriage, and the prospect of having her with him forever pleased him. Why should he give his lovely daughter to a chicken-livered suitor?

At last the day came when Prince Michael presented himself to the king. He told the king that he had loved the princess since she was a child and that he had reason to believe that the princess loved him. "Did she not give me her sleeve to wear in the last jousting tournament?" he asked. "Did she not throw me her bouquet when I won it?"

"That is all very well," said the king, "but are you a man of courage and strength?"

"I have always won in the jousts," he said. "Have you not seen me unseat my opponent every time?"

"Tut, tut," said the king. "That is nothing! I did it myself as a young man." Then the king looked at the prince sternly. "You know of my monster?"

The prince replied, "Aye, your majesty. Everyone knows of the king's monster."

"Then if you wrestle with and overcome the monster," said the king, "I will accept your suit for the princess's hand."

To the king's great surprise, the prince said, "I accept the challenge, your majesty. Where is the monster?"

The king seemed greatly astonished. "Why-ah! Why-ah!" he stammered. "In the dungeon, of course."

The king rang a bell, and a servant appeared. Then the king handed him a large bunch of keys and said, "Take this man to the dungeon."

"To the dungeon!" exclaimed the servant.

"To the dungeon," said the king.

The servant bowed and motioned to the prince to follow him.

In the great hall they met the princess. Prince Michael dropped on his knee before her. "Dear Princess Gabriella," he said, "I have come to ask your father for your hand in marriage, for I have loved you long and devotedly."

"And I, you," said the princess. Giving her hand to the prince and motioning him to rise, she said, "Where are you going?"

"To wrestle with the king's monster," the prince replied, "in order to prove my courage and my strength."

"Oh," cried the princess, "where is the monster?"

"The king said the monster is in the dungeon," the prince replied. "We are on our way."

"Are you not afraid?" cried the princess.

"My love for you, Gabriella, is greater than my fear of the monster," the prince answered.

The princess lifted her face for a kiss. "You are my true love," she said, "and I shall go with you. Whither thou goest, I shall go."

Reluctantly the prince agreed. He and the princess followed the servant down, down, down the circular stairs until they finally reached the dungeon.

The servant selected a large key and placed it in the keyhole. The door of the dungeon creaked as it opened. The prince and the princess shuddered as they felt the chilling cold of the dungeon. An odour of moldy straw filled their nostrils. Suddenly the princess let out a cry, for the wind screeching around a corner of the palace sounded like an animal in pain.

"There is nothing to fear," said the prince, placing his arm around the princess. "It is just the wind."

"Let us hope so," said the princess.

Very little light entered the dungeon through the one window. In the gloom it appeared to be empty. Together the prince and the princess looked around. They searched in the corners and under the stone bench. They found nothing either dead or alive.

Then suddenly, from out of the pile of straw, came a tiny, little field mouse. When it realized that it was not alone, it sat up and, trembling, gazed at the prince and princess. They turned to each other, burst into laughter, and fell into each other's arms.

The prince pointed to the little mouse and said, "Behold the king's monster!"

The princess wept with joy. Then, wiping away her tears, she said, "It was all a hoax. There never was a monster. It was just my father's story."

Of course, when it was known that the king's monster was the king's story, everyone began saying they never had believed it in the first place. The people who had complained of the monster's roaring discovered that it was just the wind roaring in their own chimneys. The people who thought the air was polluted said, "What lovely air we have."

"Naturally," said Dick Blabbermouth, "the king has fired the cook for throwing the garbage into the moat."

This time Dick Blabbermouth was believed.

The prince and the princess were married with great festivities. There was dancing and feasting. Bells rang throughout the land, and there was joy in both their realms.

Even after, when children came running home with terrible, frightening tales, their mothers would say, "Remember the king's monster?"

Did You Feed My Cow?

This is a call and response poem. Once you
have read it to the children, they can
respond chorally to your questions. Actions
can be added, or the children can clap along
with the rhythm.

"Did you feed my cow?"
  "Yes, Mam!"
"Will you tell me how?"
  "Yes, Mam!"
"Oh, what did you give her?"
  "Corn an' hay."
"Oh, what did you give her?"
  "Corn an' hay."

"Did you milk her good?"
  "Yes, Mam!"
"Did you do like you should?"
  "Yes, Mam!"
"Oh, how did you milk her?"
  "Swish! Swish! Swish!"
"Oh, how did you milk her?"
  "Swish! Swish! Swish!"

TRADITIONAL

Greyling

By Jane Yolen

Before the story

Discuss the concept of mermaids and other half-people, half-creatures. Ask the children, "Where would such characters live? Who would be their friends? What kinds of problems would they have?"

After the story

Ask the children, "Do you think the parents were sad after the boy became a seal? Would the seal boy miss his parents now that he had returned to the sea? Why wouldn't the villagers help the woman and the boy?"

Once on a time when wishes were aplenty, a fisherman and his wife lived by the side of the sea. All that they ate came out of the sea. Their hut was covered with the finest mosses that kept them cool in the summer and warm in the winter. And there was nothing they needed or wanted except a child.

Each morning, when the moon slipped down behind the water, and the sun rose up behind the plains, the wife would say to the fisherman, "You have your boat and your nets and your lines. But I have no baby to hold in my arms." And again, in the evening, it was the same. She would weep and wail and rock the cradle that stood by the hearth. But year in and year out the cradle stayed empty.

Now the fisherman was also sad that they had no child. But he kept his sorrow to himself so that his wife would not know his grief and thus double her own. Indeed, he would leave the hut each morning with a breath of song and return each night with a whistle on his lips. His nets were full but his heart was empty, yet he never told his wife.

One sunny day, when the beach was a tan thread spun between sea and plain, the fisherman as usual went down to his boat. But this day he found a small grey seal stranded on the sand bar, crying for its own.

The fisherman looked up the beach and down. He looked in front of him and behind. And he looked to the town on the great grey cliffs that sheered off into the sea. But there were no other seals in sight.

So he shrugged his shoulders and took off his shirt. Then he dipped it into the water and wrapped the seal pup carefully into its folds.

"You have no father and you have no mother," he said. "And I have no child. So you shall come home with me."

And the fisherman did no fishing that day but brought the seal pup, wrapped in his shirt, straight home to his wife.

When she saw him coming home early with no shirt on, the fisherman's wife ran out of the hut. Then she looked wonderingly at the bundle which he held in his arms.

"It is nothing," he said, "but a seal pup I found stranded in the shallows and longing for its own. I thought we could give it love and care until it is old enough to seek its kin."

The fisherman's wife nodded and took the bundle. Then she uncovered the wrapping and gave a loud cry. "Nothing!" she said. "You call this nothing?"

The fisherman looked. Instead of a seal lying

in the folds, there was a strange child with great grey eyes and silvery grey hair, smiling up at him.

The fisherman wrung his hands. "It is a selchie," he cried. "I have heard of them. They are men upon the land and seals in the sea. I thought it was but a tale."

"Then he shall remain a man upon the land," said the fisherman's wife, clasping the child in her arms, "for I shall never let him return to the sea."

"Never," agreed the fisherman, for he knew how his wife had wanted a child. And in his secret heart, he wanted one, too. Yet he felt, somehow, it was wrong.

"We shall call him Greyling," said the fisherman's wife, "for his eyes and hair are the colour of a storm-coming sky. Greyling, though he has brought sunlight into our home."

And though they still lived by the side of the water in a hut covered with mosses that kept them warm in the winter and cool in the summer, the boy Greyling was never allowed in the sea.

He grew from a child to a lad. He grew from a lad to a young man. He gathered driftwood for his mother's hearth and searched the tide pools for shells for her mantel. He mended his father's nets and tended his father's boat. But though he often stood by the shore or high in the town on the great grey cliffs, looking and longing and grieving his heart for what he did not really know, he never went into the sea.

Then one wind-wailing morning, just fifteen years from the day that Greyling had been found, a great storm blew up suddenly in the North. It was such a storm as had never been seen before; the sky turned nearly black and even the fish had trouble swimming. The wind pushed huge waves onto the shore. The waters gobbled up the little hut on the beach. And Greyling and the fisherman's wife were forced to flee to the town high on the great grey cliffs. There they looked down at the roiling, boiling sea. Far from shore they spied the fisherman's boat, its sails flapping like the wings of a wounded gull. And clinging to the broken mast was the fisherman himself, sinking deeper with every wave.

The fisherman's wife gave a terrible cry. "Will no one save him?" she called to the people of the town who had gathered on the edge of the cliff. "Will no one save my own dear husband who is all of life to me?"

But the townsmen looked away. There was no man there who dared risk his life in that sea, even to save a drowning soul.

"Will no one at all save him?" she cried out again.

"Let the boy go," said one old man, pointing at Greyling with his stick. "He looks strong enough."

But the fisherman's wife clasped Greyling in her arms and held his ears with her hands. She did not want him to go into the sea. She was afraid he would never return.

"Will no one save my own dear heart?" cried the fisherman's wife for a third and last time.

But shaking their heads, the people of the town edged to their houses and shut their doors and locked their windows and set their backs to the ocean and their faces to the fires that glowed in every hearth.

"I will save him, Mother," cried Greyling, "or die as I try."

Before she could tell him to stop, he broke from her grasp and dived from the top of the great cliffs, down, down, down into the tumbling sea.

"He will surely sink," whispered the women as they ran from their warm fires to watch.

"He will certainly drown," called the men as they took down their spyglasses from the shelves.

They gathered on the cliffs and watched the boy dive down into the sea.

As Greyling disappeared beneath the waves, little fingers of foam tore at his clothes. They snatched his shirt, his trousers and his shoes and sent them bubbling away to the shore. And as Greyling went deeper beneath the waves, even his skin seemed to slough off till he swam, free at last, in the sleek grey coat of a great grey seal.

The selchie had returned to the sea.

But the people of the town did not see this. All they saw was the diving boy disappearing under the waves and then, farther out, a large seal swimming towards the boat that wallowed in the sea. The sleek grey seal, with no effort at all, eased the fisherman to the shore, though the waves were wild and bright with foam. And then, with a final salute, it turned its back on the land and headed joyously out to sea.

The fisherman's wife hurried down to the sand. And behind her followed the people of the town. They searched up the beach and down, but they did not find the boy.

"A brave son," said the men when they found his shirt, for they thought he was certainly drowned.

"A very brave son," said the women when they found his shoes, for they thought him lost for sure.

"Has he really gone?" asked the fisherman's wife of her husband when at last they were alone.

"Yes, quite gone," the fisherman said to her. "Gone where his heart calls, gone to the great wide sea. And though my heart grieves at his leaving, it tells me this way is best."

The fisherman's wife sighed. And then she cried. But at last she agreed that, perhaps, it was best. "For he is both man and seal," she said. "And though we cared for him for a while, now he must care for himself." And she never cried again.

So once more they lived alone by the side of the sea in a new little hut which was covered with mosses to keep them warm in the winter and cool in the summer.

Yet, once a year, a great grey seal is seen at night near the fisherman's home. And the people in town talk of it, and wonder. But seals do come to the shore and men do go to the sea; and so the townfolk do not dwell upon it very long.

But it is no ordinary seal. It is Greyling himself come home—come to tell his parents tales of the lands that lie far beyond the waters, and to sing them songs of the wonders that lie far beneath the sea.

Little Cat

This dialogue poem can be written on chart paper for two-part choral speaking. Have Group 1 read aloud the first verse and Group 2 the second verse.

For discussion: "Why didn't the cat dream about mice but about a dish of fish and a bowl of cream? When might the little cat dream about mice or rats?"

Little Cat,
Little Cat,
As you sat
On the mat,
Did you dream
Of a mouse,
Or a GREAT BIG RAT?

Oh, no!
Not so!
For I always dream
Of a dish
Full of fish
And a bowl
Full of cream!

LAURA E. RICHARDS

The Girl Who Loved the Wind

By Jane Yolen

Before the story

Make a list of times when the wind is kind
and when the wind is not kind, e.g. flying
kites, blowing hats off people's heads.

or

Ask, "How do we know when the wind is
present? What is the angriest wind you can
remember? What is the softest wind you
can remember? What is the loudest wind
you can remember? What is the quietest
wind you can remember?"

After the story

The class can discuss what kind of life
Danina might have led after she was carried
away by the wind. They could paint what
she saw as she flew above the world.

Read the wind's songs aloud and have the
children create the wind's sounds quietly
under your words. Have the children join in
on the line "I am not always kind"; build
it louder and louder, then have the sound
fade away.

Once many years ago in a country far to
the east there lived a wealthy merchant.
He was a widower and had an only
daughter named Danina. She was dainty and
beautiful, and he loved her more than he loved
all of his treasures.

Because Danina was his only child, the
merchant wanted to keep her from anything
that might hurt or harm her in any way, and so
he decided to shut her away from the world.

When Danina was still an infant, her father
brought her to a great house which he had built
on the shore of the sea. On three sides of the
house rose three huge walls. And on the fourth
side was the sea itself.

In this lovely, lonely place Danina grew up
knowing everything that was in her father's
heart but nothing of the world.

In her garden grew every kind of fair fruit
and flower, for so her father willed it. And on
her table was every kind of fresh fish and fowl,
for so her father ordered. In her room were
the finest furnishings. Gaily coloured books and
happy music, light dancing and bright paintings,
filled her days. And the servants were instructed
always to smile, never to say no, and to be
cheerful all through the year. So her father
wished it and so it was done. And for many
years, nothing sad touched Danina in any way.

Yet one spring day, as Danina stood by her
window gazing at the sea, a breeze blew salt
across the waves. It whipped her hair about her
face. It blew in the corners of her room. And
as it moved, it whistled a haunting little tune.

Danina had never heard such a thing before.
It was sad, but it was beautiful. It intrigued
her. It beguiled her. It caused her to sigh and
clasp her hands.

"Who are you?" asked Danina.

And the wind answered:

> *Who am I?*
> *I call myself the wind.*
> *I slap at ships and sparrows.*
> *I sough through broken windows.*
> *I shepherd snow and sandstorms.*
> *I am not always kind.*

"How peculiar," said Danina. "Here you
merely rustle the trees and play with the leaves
and calm the birds in their nests."

"*I am not always kind,*" said the wind again.

"Everyone here is always kind. Everyone
here is always happy."

"*Nothing is always,*" said the wind.

"My life is always," said Danina. "Always
happy."

"*But life is not always happy,*" said the wind.

"Mine is," said Danina.

"*How sad,*" whispered the wind from a
corner.

"What do you mean?" asked Danina. But the
wind only whirled through the window carrying
one of her silken scarves, and before she could

speak again, he had blown out to sea.

Days went by, happy days. Yet sometimes in her room, Danina would try to sing the wind's song. She could not quite remember the words or recall the tune, but its strangeness haunted her.

Finally, one morning, she asked her father: "Why isn't life always happy?"

"Life *is* always happy," replied her father.

"That's what I told him," said Danina.

"Told who?" asked her father. He was suddenly frightened, frightened that someone would take his daughter away.

"The wind," said Danina.

"The wind does not talk," said her father.

"He called himself the wind," she replied.

But her father did not understand. And so when a passing fisherman found Danina's scarf far out at sea and returned it to the merchant's house, he was rewarded with a beating, for the merchant suspected that the fisherman was the one who called himself the wind.

Then one summer day, weeks later, when the sun was reflected in the petals of the flowers, Danina strolled in her garden. Suddenly the wind leaped over the high wall and pushed and pulled at the tops of the trees. He sang his strange song, and Danina clasped her hands and sighed.

"Who are you?" she whispered.

"*Who am I?*" said the wind, and he sang:

> *Who am I?*
> *I call myself the wind.*
> *I've worked the sails of windmills.*
> *I've whirled the sand in deserts.*
> *I've wrecked ten thousand galleons.*
> *I am not always kind.*

"I knew it was you," said Danina. "But no one believed me."

And the wind danced around the garden and made the flowers bow.

He caressed the birds in the trees and played gently with the feathers on their wings.

"You say you are not always kind," said Danina. "You say you have done many unkind things. But all I see is that you are gentle and good."

"*But not always,*" reminded the wind. "*Nothing is always.*"

"Is it sad then beyond the wall?"

"*Sometimes sad and sometimes happy,*" said the wind.

"But different each day?" said Danina.

"*Very different.*"

"How strange," Danina said. "Here things are always the same. Always beautiful. Happy. Good."

"*How sad,*" said the wind. "*How dull.*" And he leaped over the wall and blew out into the world.

"Come back," shouted Danina, rushing to the wall. But her voice was lost against the stones.

Just then her father came into the garden. He saw his daughter standing by the wall and crying to the top. He ran over to her. "Who are you calling? Who has been here?" he demanded.

"The wind," said Danina, her eyes bright with memory. "He sang me his song."

"The wind does not sing," said her father. "Only men and birds sing."

"This was no bird," said his daughter.

"Then," thought her father, "it must have been a man." And he resolved to keep Danina from the garden.

Locked out of her garden, Danina began to wander up and down the long corridors of the house, and what once had seemed like a palace to her began to feel like a prison. Everything seemed false. The happy smiles of the servants she saw as smiles of pity for her ignorance. The gay dancing seemed to hide broken hearts. The bright paintings hid sad thoughts. And soon Danina found herself thinking of the wind at every moment, humming his song to the walls. His song about the world—sometimes happy, sometimes sad, but always full of change and challenge.

Her father, who was not cruel but merely foolish, could not keep her locked up completely. Once a day, for an hour, he allowed Danina to walk along the beach. But three maidservants walked before her. Three manservants walked behind. And the merchant himself watched from a covered chair.

One chilly day in the fall, when the tops of the waves rolled in white to the shore, Danina strolled on the beach. She pulled her cape around her for warmth. And the three maidservants before her and the three manservants behind shivered in the cold. Her father in his covered chair pulled his blanket to his chin and stared out to sea. He was cold and unhappy, but he was more afraid to leave Danina alone.

Suddenly the wind blew across the caps of the waves, tossing foam into the air.

Danina turned to welcome him, stretching out her arms. The cape billowed behind her like the wings of a giant bird.

"Who are you?" thundered Danina's father, jumping out of his chair.

The wind spun around Danina and sang:

Who am I?
I call myself the wind.
I am not always happy.
I am not always kind.

"Nonsense," roared Danina's father. "Everyone here is always happy and kind. I shall arrest you for trespassing." And he shouted, "GUARDS!"

But before the guards could come, Danina had spread her cape on the water. Then she stepped onto it, raised one corner, and waved goodbye to her father. The blowing wind filled the cape's corner like the sail of a ship.

And before Danina's father had time to call out, before he had time for one word of repentance, she was gone. And the last thing he saw was the billowing cape as Danina and the wind sailed far to the west into the ever-changing world.

Calico Pie

This poem provides a perfect listening
experience for the children. Each verse is
about different creatures, and the common
refrain lets the children join in as soon as
they are able.

Calico Pie,
The little Birds fly
Down to the calico tree,
Their wings were blue,
And they sang "Tilly-loo!"
Till away they flew—
And they never came back to me!
They never came back!
They never came back!
They never came back to me!

Calico Ban,
The little Mice ran,
To be ready in time for tea,
Flippity flup,
They drank it all up,
And danced in the cup—
But they never came back to me!
They never came back!
They never came back!
They never came back to me!

Calico Jam,
The little Fish swam,
Over the syllabub sea,
He took off his hat,
To the Sole and the Sprat,
And the Willeby-wat—
But he never came back to me!
He never came back!
He never came back!
He never came back to me!

Calico Drum,
The Grasshoppers come,
The Butterfly, Beetle, and Bee,
Over the ground,
Around and around,
With a hop and a bound—
But they never came back!
They never came back!
They never came back!
They never came back to me!

EDWARD LEAR

A Baby Sister for Frances

By Russell Hoban

Before the story

Say/read this poem to the pupils:
"*Plinketty, plinketty, plinketty, plink
Here is the dishrag that's under the sink.
Here are the buckets and brushes and me,
Plinketty, plinketty, plinketty, plee.*"

   Ask the children, "Why do we sing songs when we are all alone? Who do you think might be singing this song?"

After the story

Ask the children, "Why do you think Frances wanted to run away? Are there times when you become annoyed or upset? How do you handle people around you when you feel like that? Do you have a private, cozy place to go when you feel like that? How did Frances's family try to make her feel better? What are some good points about having brothers and sisters? What things does having a new baby change in a home? Do you ever find it difficult to get big people's attention? How do you feel? What do you do? Do you have special possessions like Frances's blanket and alligator doll? What are they? When you pack a lunch, what do you like to put in it? What is the favourite breakfast of each person in your home?"

   Have the students say the "Plinketty..." poem again.

I t was a quiet evening. Father was reading his newspaper. Mother was feeding Gloria, the new baby. Frances was sitting under the kitchen sink. She was singing a little song:

   *Plinketty, plinketty, plinketty, plink,
   Here is the dishrag that's under the sink.
   Here are the buckets and brushes and
      me,
   Plinketty, plinketty, plinketty, plee.*

She stopped the song and listened. Nobody said anything.

   Frances went to her room and took some gravel out of the drawer where she had been saving it. She put the gravel into her empty coffee can and put the lid back on the can. Frances marched into the living room and rattled the gravel in the can. As she marched she sang a marching song:

   Here we go marching, rattley bang!

"Please don't do that, Frances," said Father.

   Frances stopped. "All right," she said. She went back to the kitchen and sat down under the sink.

   Mother came in, carrying Gloria. "Why are you sitting under the sink?" said Mother.

   "I like it here," said Frances. "It's cozy."

   "Would you like to help me put Gloria to bed?" said Mother.

   "How much allowance does Gloria get?" said Frances.

   "She is too little to have an allowance," said Father. "Only big girls like you get allowances. Isn't it nice to be a big sister?"

   "May I have a penny along with my nickel now that I am a big sister?" said Frances.

   "Yes," said Father. "Now your allowance will be six cents a week because you are a big sister."

   "Thank you," said Frances.

   "I know a girl who gets seventeen cents a week. She gets three nickels and two pennies."

"Well," said Father, "it's time for bed now." Father picked Frances up from under the sink and gave her a piggyback ride to bed.

Mother and Father tucked her in and kissed her good night.

"I need my tiny special blanket," said Frances.

Mother gave her the tiny special blanket.

"And I need my tricycle and my sled and both teddy bears and my alligator doll," said Frances.

Father brought in the tricycle and the sled and both teddy bears and the alligator doll.

Mother and Father kissed her good night again and Frances went to sleep.

In the morning Frances got up and washed and began to dress for school. "Is my blue dress ready for me to wear?" said Frances.

"Oh, dear," said Mother, "I was so busy with Gloria that I did not have time to iron it, so you'll have to wear the yellow one." Mother buttoned Frances up the back. Then she brushed her hair and put a new ribbon in it and put her breakfast on the table.

"Why did you put sliced bananas on the oatmeal?" said Frances. "Did you forget that I like raisins?"

"No, I did not forget," said Mother, "but you finished up the raisins yesterday and I have not been out shopping yet."

"Well," said Frances, "things are not very good around here anymore. No clothes to wear. No raisins for the oatmeal. I think maybe I'll run away."

"Finish your breakfast," said Mother. "It is almost time for the school bus."

"What time will dinner be tonight?" said Frances.

"Half past six," said Mother.

"Then I will have plenty of time to run away after dinner," said Frances, and she kissed her mother goodbye and went to school.

After dinner that evening Frances packed her little knapsack very carefully. She put in her tiny special blanket and her alligator doll. She took all of the nickels and pennies out of her bank, for travel money, and she took her good luck coin for good luck. Then she took a box of prunes from the kitchen and five chocolate sandwich cookies.

"Well," said Frances, "it is time to say goodbye. I am on my way. Goodbye."

"Where are you running away to?" said Father.

"I think that under the dining-room table is the best place," said Frances. "It's cozy, and the kitchen is near if I run out of cookies."

"That is a good place to run away to," said Mother, "but I'll miss you."

"I'll miss you too," said Father.

"Well," said Frances, "goodbye," and she ran away.

Father sat down with his newspaper.

Mother took up the sweater she was knitting.

Father put down the newspaper. "You know," he said, "it is not the same house without Frances."

"That is just *exactly* what I was thinking," said Mother. "The place seems lonesome and empty without her."

Frances sat under the dining-room table and ate her prunes.

"Even Gloria," said Mother, "as small as she is, can feel the difference."

"I can hear her crying a little right now," said Father.

"Well," said Mother, "a girl looks up to an older sister. You know that."

Father picked up his newspaper. Then he put it down again. "I miss the songs that Frances used to sing," he said.

I was *so* fond of those little songs," said Mother. "Do you remember the one about the tomato? 'What does the tomato say, early in the dawn?' " sang Mother.

" 'Time to be all red again, now that night is gone,' " sang Father. "Yes," he said, "that is a good one, but my favourite has always been: 'When the wasps and the bumblebees have a party, nobody comes that can't buzz. . . .' "

"Well," said Mother, "we shall just have to get used to a quiet house now."

Frances ate three of the sandwich cookies and put the other two aside for later. She began to sing:

> *I am poor and hungry here, eating*
> *prunes and rice.*
> *Living all alone is not really very nice.*

She had no rice, but chocolate sandwich cookies did not sound right for the song.

"I can almost hear her now," said Father, humming the tune that Frances had just sung. "She has a charming voice."

"It is just not a *family* without Frances," said Mother. "Babies are very nice. Goodness knows I *like* babies, but a baby is not a family."

"Isn't that a fact!" said Father.

"A family is *everybody all together*."

"Remember," said Mother, "how I used to

say, 'Think how lucky the new baby will be to have a sister like Frances'?"

"I remember that very well," said Father, "and I hope that Gloria turns out to be as clever and good as Frances."

"With a big sister like Frances to help her along, she ought to turn out just fine," said Mother.

"I'd like to hear from Frances," said Father, "just to know how she is getting along in her new place."

"I'd like to hear from Frances too," said Mother, "and I'm not sure the sleeves are right on this sweater I'm knitting for her."

"Hello," called Frances from the dining room. "I am calling on the telephone. Hello, hello, this is me. Is that you?"

"Hello," said Mother. "This is us. How are you?"

"I am fine," said Frances. "This is a nice place, but you miss your family when you're away. How are you?"

"We are all well," said Father, "but we miss you too."

"I will be home soon," said Frances, and she hung up.

"She said that she will be home soon," said Father.

"That is good news indeed," said Mother. "I think I'll bake a cake."

Frances put on her knapsack and sang a little travelling song:

> Big sisters really have to stay
> At home, not travel far away,
> Because everybody misses them
> And wants to hug-and-kisses them.

"I'm not sure about that last rhyme," said Frances as she arrived in the living room and took off her knapsack.

"That's a good enough rhyme," said Father.

"I like it fine," said Mother, and they both hugged and kissed her.

"What kind of cake are you baking?" said Frances to Mother.

"Chocolate," said Mother.

"It's too bad that Gloria's too little to have some," said Frances, "but when she's a big girl like me, she can have chocolate cake too."

"Oh, yes," said Mother, "you may be sure that there will always be plenty of chocolate cake around here."

A Nonsense Alphabet

As you read this alphabet poem to the
children, have them listen to each stanza
while you signal, so the children can call out
each letter at the appropriate time.

A was an ape,
   Who stole some white tape
   And tied up his toes
   In four beautiful bows.
          a!
      Funny old Ape!

B was a bat,
   Who slept all the day
   And fluttered about
   When the sun went away.
          b!
      Brown little Bat!

C was a camel,
   You rode on his hump
   And if you fell off,
   You came down such a bump!
          c!
      What a high Camel!

D was a dove
   Who lived in a wood
   With such pretty soft wings,
   And so gentle and good.
          d!
      Dear little Dove!

E was an eagle
   Who sat on the rocks
   And looked down on the fields
   And the far away flocks.
          e!
      Beautiful Eagle!

F was a fan
   Made of beautiful stuff
   And when it was used
   It went—Puffy-puff-puff!
          f!
      Nice little Fan!

G was a gooseberry
   Perfectly red;
   To be made into jam
   And eaten with bread.
          g!
      Gooseberry red!

H was a heron
   Who stood in a stream
   The length of his neck
   And his legs, was extreme.
          h!
      Long-legged Heron!

I was an inkstand
   Which stood on a table
   With a nice pen to write with,
   When we were able!
          i!
      Neat little Inkstand!

J was a jug,
   So pretty and white
   With fresh water in it
   At morning and night.
          j!
      Nice little Jug!

K was a kingfisher,
Quickly he flew
So bright and so pretty,
Green, purple and blue.
k!
Kingfisher, blue!

L was a lily
So white and so sweet
To see it and smell it
Was quite a nice treat!
l!
Beautiful Lily!

M was a man,
Who walked round and round,
And he wore a long coat
That came down to the ground.
m!
Funny old Man!

N was a nut
So smooth and so brown,
And when it was ripe
It fell tumble-dum-down.
n!
Nice little Nut!

O was an oyster
Who lived in his shell,
If you left him alone
He felt perfectly well.
o!
Open-mouthed Oyster!

P was a polly
All red, blue and green
The most beautiful polly
That ever was seen.
p!
Poor little Polly!

Q was a quill
Made into a pen,
But I do not know where
And I cannot say when.
q!
Nice little Quill!

R was a rattlesnake
Rolled up so tight,
Those who saw him ran quickly
For fear he should bite.
r!
Rattlesnake bite!

S was a screw
To screw down a box
And then it was fastened
Without any locks.
s!
Valuable Screw!

T was a thimble
Of silver so bright
When placed on the finger
It fitted so tight!
t!
Nice little Thimble!

U was an upper-coat
Woolly and warm
To wear over all
In the snow or the storm.
u!
What a nice Upper-coat!

V was a veil
With a border upon it
And a riband to tie it
All round a pink bonnet.
v!
Pretty green Veil!

W was a watch
Where in letters of gold
The hour of the day
You might always behold.
w!
Beautiful Watch!

X was King Xerxes
Who wore on his head
A mighty large turban,
Green, yellow and red.
x!
Look at King Xerxes!

Y was a yak
From the land of Thibet
Except his white tail
He was all black as jet.
y!
Look at the Yak!

Z was a zebra,
All striped white and black,
And if he were tame
You might ride on his back.
z!
Pretty striped Zebra!

EDWARD LEAR

The Three Sillies

By Anne Rockwell

Before the story

Ask the children, "When do you enjoy
'acting silly'? What makes behaviour 'silly'
to you? Do adults ever act silly? What is
the silliest comedy routine you have ever
seen on television or film? Do you remember
a 'silly' story that you have heard?"

After the story

Ask the children, "Why were the people in
the story so silly? What would you have
done if you had been in these silly
situations? How could you have persuaded
the villagers that the moon wasn't really
in the water?"

Once upon a time there was a farmer and
his wife, and they had one daughter
who was being courted by a gentleman.
Every night he used to come for supper, and
the daughter used to go down to the cellar to
get a jug of cider.

One evening she went down, and she
happened to look up at the ceiling while the jug
was filling, and she saw a big hatchet stuck in
one of the beams. It must have been there a
long time, but somehow she had never noticed
it before, and she began thinking. And she
thought, "Suppose we were to be married and
we were to have a son, and we sent him down
to the cellar to get cider, and that hatchet was
to fall on his head, what a dreadful thing that
would be!" And she sat down and began to cry.

Well, upstairs they began to wonder what
was keeping her, so her mother went down to
see. She found the daughter sitting on the
bench crying and the cider running all over
the floor.

"Why, whatever is the matter?" said her
mother.

"Oh, mother!" said the daughter. "Look at
that hatchet! Suppose my sweetheart and I got
married and had a son, and we sent him down

to the cellar to get cider, and that hatchet
fell on his head, what a dreadful thing that
would be!"

"Oh, yes, what a dreadful thing it would be!"
said the mother, and she sat down alongside
the daughter and started crying, too.

Then after a bit the father began to wonder
why they didn't come back, and he went down
to the cellar to look for himself. There the two
sat crying and the cider running all over
the floor.

"Whatever is the matter?" said he.

"Why," said the mother, "look at that
hatchet! Just suppose our daughter and her
sweetheart got married and suppose they had a
son, and he came down to the cellar to get
cider and that hatchet fell on his head. What a
dreadful thing that would be!"

"So it would! So it would!" said the father,
and sat down beside his wife and daughter and
started crying, too.

Now the gentleman got tired of sitting in the
kitchen all by himself, so he went down to the
cellar to see what was taking so long. There sat
all three, crying side by side, and the cider
running all over the floor. And he ran and
turned off the tap, and said, "Whatever are you

three doing, sitting there crying and letting the cider run all over the floor?"

"Oh," said the father, "look at that hatchet! Suppose you and our daughter got married and suppose you had a son, and he came down to the cellar to get cider and that hatchet fell on his head!" And they all three started crying again, worse than before.

Then the gentleman burst out laughing. He pulled down the hatchet and said, "I've travelled a long way, but I've never seen three such big sillies as you before. I will start out on my travels again, and when I find three bigger sillies than you three, I'll come back and marry your daughter." So he said goodbye and set out on his travels.

Well, he travelled a long way, and he came to a house that had grass growing on the roof. A woman was trying to get her cow to go up the ladder and on to the roof to eat the grass, and the poor thing would not go. So the gentleman asked the woman what she was doing.

"Why, look!" she said. "Just look at that beautiful good grass. I'm going to get the cow up on the roof to eat it. She'll be quite safe there, for I shall tie a rope around her neck and pass it down the chimney and tie the other end to my wrist as I go about the house. That way she can't fall off the roof without my knowing it."

"Oh, you poor silly!" said the gentleman. "You should cut the grass and throw it down to the cow."

But the woman thought it easier to get the cow up than the grass down, so she pushed her and coaxed her and got her up. Then she tied a rope around the cow's neck, passed it down the chimney, and fastened the other end to her wrist. The gentleman went on his way, but he hadn't gone far when the cow tumbled off the roof and hung by the rope tied around her neck. The weight of the cow at the other end of the rope that was tied to her wrist pulled the woman up the chimney, and she stuck halfway, all smothered in soot.

Well, that was one big silly.

The gentleman journeyed on until nightfall, and he went to an inn to spend the night. The inn was so full they had to put him in a double-bedded room, and another traveller was to share the bed. The other man was a very pleasant fellow, but in the morning, when they were getting dressed, the gentleman was surprised to see the other fellow hang his trousers on the knobs of the chest of drawers and run across the room and try to jump into them. He tried over and over again and just couldn't manage it, and the gentleman wondered what he was doing it for.

At last he stopped and wiped his face with a handkerchief. "Oh, dear," he said, "I do think trousers are the most awkward clothes there are. Who could have invented such things? It takes me the best part of an hour to get into them every morning, and I get so hot and tired. How do you manage yours?"

The gentleman burst out laughing and showed him how to put them on. The other fellow was much obliged to him, for he said he never would have thought of doing it that way.

So that was another big silly.

Then the gentleman went on his travels again. He came to a village, and outside that village there was a pond, and around the pond there was a crowd of people. And they all had rakes and brooms and pitchforks reaching into the pond, and the gentleman asked what was the matter.

"Why," they said, "matter enough! Moon's tumbled into the pond, and we can't get it out!"

So the gentleman burst out laughing and told them to look up into the sky for it was only the moon's reflection in the water. But they wouldn't listen to him and abused him most shamefully, so he got away as quickly as he could.

Well, there were a whole lot of sillies bigger than the three at home. So the gentleman turned back and married the farmer's daughter, and if they didn't live happily ever after, that's got nothing to do with you or me.

Oodles of Noodles

This poem is full of word play and should
be read for the linguistic feeling of the
rhyme and the invented words.

Encourage the children to invent fun
words using the patterns in the poem, e.g.
favourite foodles, pizza whizza, hamboogle.

I love noodles. Give me oodles.
Make a mound up to the sun.
Noodles are my favorite foodles.
I eat noodles by the ton.

LUCIA AND JAMES L. HYMES, JR.

The Terrible Nung Gwama

ADAPTED BY ED YOUNG

Before the story

Ask the children to list all the scary
creatures they have heard about in stories
and films (e.g. vampires, etc.). Explain that
this story from China long ago is about a
terrible creature, the Nung Gwama.

After the story

This story can be the basis for a drama
lesson. Tell the children that they are
another village being terrorized by another
Nung Gwama. Through role-playing, help
them to create a plan for handling the
creature by asking the questions, "What
stories have you heard about the creature's
activity? How will you approach it? What
kind of trap will you have? Who will draw
the creature to the trap?"

Once, long ago in China, a poor young
woman decided to take some cakes to her
venerable parents. It was a long way
from her house to theirs, so she went as fast as
she could on her tiny feet.

The dusty road was empty. It wound through
bright green fields where rice was growing.
Suddenly, as the woman passed a grove of
bamboo trees by the side of the road, out
jumped a terrible monster. "Aargh! Aargh!"
it roared.

She knew at once that it was a Nung Gwama,
for it had the body of a bull and a head as big
as an oven, and it gnashed its teeth and
stretched out its claws in a horrible way. And
she also knew that it was very fierce, for of all
things the Nung Gwama delights most in eating
people.

Now, no one likes the thought of being eaten,
whether by a tiger, a snake, or a dragon. But
what strikes people as particularly repulsive
about the Nung Gwama is his *way* of eating. He
does not pick delicately at his food, disposing
of each choice morsel in a polite manner. He
just crunches and chews in the rudest way

imaginable, and gobbles up everything—hair,
head, bones and all—roaring all the while,
"Aargh! Aargh!"

Less frightening, but still horrid are his feet.
They are very fat and floppy, so that as he
walks you can hear them: *Flip. Flop. Flip.
Flop.*

It was no wonder, then, that the poor woman
sank to her knees in terror, and hid her face
from this terrible monster.

The Nung Gwama said greedily, "Give me
those delectable cakes at once."

Now, even though she was very frightened,
the poor woman's duty to her parents came
first.

"I can't do that," she said, sobbing. "They
are for my venerable parents."

"All right, then," growled the Nung Gwama.
"This very night I will come to your house and
tear you to pieces with my claws and crunch
you up with my sharp teeth and *eat* you."

At this, the woman hung her head in despair.

When, after a while, she fearfully lifted her
head and looked around her, the Nung Gwama
had vanished. But there was no doubt that he

would come back. Sure that she was about to have a painful and also an undignified death, the poor woman sat in the dust, howling with fear.

Some people passing by stopped politely to ask what was the matter.

"The terrible Nung Gwama is coming tonight to tear me to pieces and crunch me up and eat me," she told them. The people all nodded their heads. It was true, they said, she might as well prepare to die: the Nung Gwama always came when he said he would.

While they were talking, a pedlar stopped to ask why the poor woman was weeping. They told him about the Nung Gwama's threat.

The pedlar set down the bamboo baskets which hung from his carrying pole. "Here," he said to the woman. "I'll give you twenty-four sharp needles. Stick them in the door of your house, near the latch. Maybe the Nung Gwama will prick himself when he tries to open the door." And the pedlar picked up his baskets and pole and went off again.

The woman, still frightened, continued to cry. For how could a few needles save her from the Nung Gwama?

Her wails attracted a man who collected manure, which he used to fertilize his fields. He asked her what was the matter. When she told him, he thought for a while and then said, "Look, here is a little manure. Spread it on your door. Perhaps the Nung Gwama will dirty his hands with it, and go away."

The woman accepted his gift, but she cried as loudly as ever, for she thought it would be of little help against the terrible Nung Gwama.

Soon a man came by, calling out, "Snakes for sale! Snakes for sale!" He, too, stopped when he saw the weeping woman. When he asked, she told him all about the Nung Gwama, the pedlar, and the man who collected manure.

The snake seller wanted to help her, too. "Here are two of my most poisonous snakes," he said. "Put them into your washing pot. Maybe the Nung Gwama will want to wash the manure off his hands. If he tries, these snakes will bite him."

The woman thanked him for his kindness, but she was soon weeping again—for what could mere snakes do against the terrible Nung Gwama?

Then a fish seller came along. "What is all this weeping and wailing?" he asked. The woman, still howling with fright, told him the whole story.

He, too, wanted to help. So he offered the woman two fish in a cooking pot. "Take these two fish," he said. "But don't cook them, or they won't be able to bite. Just keep them in the pot. If the Nung Gwama is bitten by the snakes, maybe he will think that the cooking pot is full of warm water and he will try to bathe his sore hands in it. If he puts his hands in the pot, the fish will bite him so hard he might give up the whole idea of eating you and run away."

The woman thought that was very unlikely, but she took the fish and the cooking pot and thanked him, and went on sobbing loudly.

An egg seller came by next, shouting, "Eggs! Fine eggs for sale!" He, too, asked what was wrong. When he was told, he scratched his head and thought very hard. Then he said, "You must take these few eggs. Put them in the ashes of your fire. If the Nung Gwama is bitten by the snakes and the fish, his fingers will bleed. Then he will want to put them in the ashes to stop the bleeding. If he does that, the eggs will burst in his face. That should scare him out of his wickedness."

The woman did not think it would be so easy to scare the terrible Nung Gwama, but she thanked him and took the eggs, and then she cried louder than ever.

Next, a seller of millstones heard her crying. "I will give you this millstone," he said to her. "It is very, very heavy. You must hang it from the ceiling above your bed. If you can get the Nung Gwama to stand below it, cut the string and maybe the millstone will fall on the monster's head and knock him out. But then it may still be necessary to finish him off, so here is an iron bar with which you can beat out any life that is left in him."

By this time it was so late that the woman had to give up the idea of visiting her parents. So she sold the cakes, and with the money she paid a porter to carry all her gifts back to her own house. Penniless, hungry, and frightened, the poor woman felt sure her end was near. Nevertheless she set out all the presents exactly as she had been told to do. By the time she had prepared everything, it was very dark. She went to bed and lay there, shivering and shaking with fear.

But nothing happened. The old watchman went by, calling out the first and second watches of the night. Then he passed by again, tapping his drum for the third watch and calling out a warning to robbers.

Still nothing happened. Everything was quiet.

Then suddenly—*Flip. Flop. Flip. Flop.* It was the fat and floppy feet of the Nung Gwama, and they were just outside the door!

"*Aargh! Aargh!* Open up the door," roared the Nung Gwama. "I have come to tear you and crunch you and eat you all up."

The woman could not move, she was so frightened. The Nung Gwama rushed at the door and tore it down. But as he did, the twenty-four needles stuck in his hands and the manure dirtied them.

"Oh! Ow!" he shrieked. "What's this? Something has stung me! And what is this dirt? And the terrible smell? Well, now that I'm in, I'll soon finish you off. But first I'll wash my hands in this water.

"Yee-ow! What now?" he howled, as the snakes bit him with their poisoned fangs. "But there's a cooking pot. There will be nice warm water in that to take away this pain."

But "Ooh, ouch!" he screamed, as the fish bit his fingers. My fingers are bleeding!" And he hurried to the hearth to stop the bleeding with some ashes.

The eggs popped in his face, and the hot bits of shell flew into his eyes. "Oh, help!" cried the monster. "I'm bleeding! I can't see! Just let me get my claws on that woman. I'll certainly crunch her up for this! Where are you woman?"

"Over here," called the woman, and *flip, flop,* the Nung Gwama, who still could not see, shuffled over toward the bed. As he came close, the woman cut the string.

Down fell the millstone, right onto the Nung Gwama's back. And down fell the Nung Gwama, looking quite dead. Probably he was, but to make very sure, the woman gave him a few heavy bangs with the iron bar.

And so, instead of being eaten by a terrible monster, the woman found herself safe and sound. And there was a rich reward for the skin and bones of the Nung Gwama, which had been a danger to the whole countryside. So at last the poor woman had enough money to live happily ever after, and to take good care of her venerable parents, too.

If You Ever

This is a humorous poem to read to the
children, and to which you can add as many
"evers" and "nevers" as you want. The
class can join in on these two words. As
well, you can pattern this poem using
"bear" and "lair," or "quail" and "tail."

If you ever ever ever ever ever
   If you ever ever ever meet a whale
You must never never never never
      never
   You must never never never touch its
      tail:
For if you ever ever ever ever ever,
   If you ever ever ever touch its tail,
You will never never never never never,
   You will never never meet another
      whale.

    Anonymous

The Tutti Frutti Tree

By Monica Hughes

Before the story

Have a discussion with the children about seeds and gardens, asking the questions, "Have you planted any seeds? Do you help in the garden? What things do you wish would grow on trees?"

If the school has any flower beds, perhaps a group of children could experiment by planting some seeds.

After the story

Ask, "Where did the tree come from? Do you think Bruce knows?"

The children can paint their own tutti-frutti trees, using all the things they would like to see on their imaginary tree.

It was April. "What are you all going to plant in the garden this year?" asked Father.

"Sunflowers," said Robert, who was the eldest. "The flowers have cheerful faces and my parrot will like the seeds."

"Onions for me," said Colin. "I'll pack them in my school lunch and breathe all over any girls who hang around."

"I'll plant scarlet runners," said Maggie. "I love bright red and Mother can cook the beans for dinner."

"I'll have rows and rows of carrots," Elspeth said eagerly, "so I can feed Esmeralda." Esmeralda was an angora rabbit.

"What about us?" teased Robert.

"Oh, you can have carrots too—whatever Esmeralda can't eat!"

"Bruce, what are you going to plant in *your* garden?" Mother asked. Bruce was three.

"A tutti-frutti tree," he said, when he'd taken his thumb out of his mouth.

"A tutti-frutti tree??????" everyone asked together.

"There isn't such a thing," Robert explained kindly.

Bruce pointed at the freezer, and when Colin opened the door, they could all see the big carton of tutti-frutti ice-cream. There was a picture of all kinds of fruit on the outside.

"You can't grow ice-cream," Maggie said.

"Shut the freezer door, Colin," Mother said. "Bruce, I don't have any tutti-frutti seeds. Not a one."

But on planting day, when Robert planted sunflower seeds and Colin his onion sets, Maggie her runner beans and Elspeth the tiny carrot seeds, Bruce came out of the house with a fistful of something.

Robert dug a hole for him and Bruce put what was in his hand into the hole. There were orange and lemon and apple and grape pips, and a piece of very ripe banana that had glued itself to everything else.

"Tutti-frutti seeds," Bruce said. "*I* know."

Robert shovelled the dirt back into the hole.

It rained and rained, and then the sun came out. Before long Colin's onions were pushing up green spikes. Then the scarlet runners hooked their way up, out of the dirt, like tiny umbrella handles. Robert's sunflowers put out two big leaves each, and the carrots, little feathery ones.

In Bruce's patch there was nothing but pig-weed.

"It'll come," said Bruce.

Summer came and it was hot and everything grew like mad. Robert's sunflowers were almost two metres tall, with faces like dinner plates that followed the sun from east to west every day. Colin ate his first onions and breathed over everyone. Maggie's scarlet runners grew all over the fence. Their pods were long and thick, with fat, pinky-purple beans inside. Colin discovered they were the perfect size for pea-shooters, and then there was no peace. Esmeralda, the rabbit, ate her first carrots, and there were some left over for the boys. But there was no sign of the tutti-frutti tree.

"It'll come soon," said Bruce. He went away sucking his thumb.

"What are we going to do about Bruce's tree?" Maggie asked the others.

"What can we do?" Colin shrugged.

"If only we could *buy* a tutti-frutti tree," said Elspeth.

"You can get orange trees in pots," suggested Robert.

"Bruce wants lemons and grapes and apples and bananas and oranges. Oh, dear!" sighed Maggie.

"I've got an idea," said Robert. "Leave it to me."

Next Saturday Father and Robert went shopping and came home with a tree in a pot. It had oranges *and* lemons on it.

"That's crafty!" said Maggie. "But what about the other fruit?"

"Florist's wire," suggested Elspeth. "And green sticky tape."

They ran into the house to raid the fruit bowl. When they got back, Father had planted the orange and lemon tree in the very middle of Bruce's garden.

When Bruce woke up from his nap and trailed sleepily downstairs, everyone was in the garden admiring his tree. Bruce walked across the lawn and stood in front of his tree, his thumb in his mouth. The tree was almost as tall as he was. It had shiny, pointed leaves and oranges and lemons that glowed like suns and moons. Among the leaves were apples and little bunches of grapes. Near the bottom were six fat bananas. Bruce took his thumb out of his mouth and smiled. "I *told* you it'd come!"

He picked a bunch of grapes for Mother and a banana for Father. He gave an apple to Robert and Colin and Maggie and Elspeth. Then he sat down beside his tree and looked up at the golden oranges and yellow lemons and the grapes and apples and bananas.

"What are you thinking, Bruce?" Elspeth asked.

Bruce sighed happily. "I'm thinking that next year maybe I'll plant butterscotch ripple."

The Owl and the Pussy-Cat

This familiar poem is full of soft, gentle
words, and the sounds of this lullaby are
more important than the meaning. After
hearing the poem read aloud, the children
can join in by whispering the refrain
through the "call and response" technique.
For example:

> "What a beautiful Pussy you are,
> You are,
> You are!
> What a beautiful Pussy you are!"

The Owl and the Pussy-cat went to sea
  In a beautiful pea-green boat,
They took some honey, and plenty of
    money
  Wrapped up in a five-pound note.
The Owl looked up to the stars above,
  And sang to a small guitar,
"O lovely Pussy! O Pussy, my love,
  What a beautiful Pussy you are,
    You are,
    You are!
  What a beautiful Pussy you are!"

Pussy said to the Owl, "You elegant
    fowl!
  How charmingly sweet you sing!
O let us be married! too long we have
    tarried:
  But what shall we do for a ring?"
They sailed away, for a year and a day,
  To the land where the Bong-tree
    grows,
And there in a wood a Piggy-wig stood,
  With a ring at the end of his nose,
    His nose,
    His nose,
  With a ring at the end of his nose.

"Dear Pig, are you willing to sell for one
    shilling
  Your ring?" Said the Piggy, "I will."
So they took it away, and were married
    next day
  By the Turkey who lives on the hill.
They dined on mince, and slices of
    quince,
  Which they ate with a runcible spoon;
And hand in hand, on the edge of the
    sand,
  They danced by the light of the moon,
    The moon,
    The moon,
They danced by the light of the moon.

EDWARD LEAR

When the Drum Sang

By Anne Rockwell

Before the story

Have the children sit in a circle and play
some rhythm games. Begin by selecting a
child's name and beating out the rhythm
on the floor with your hands, e.g. Car - o -
lyn (TUM- tum - tum, TUM - tum - tum).
The children can find the rhythm for their
own names and create that rhythm with
their hands. Everyone can join in, and
several names can be chosen to make a
story.

After the story

The teacher can role-play the parent
searching for the daughter, and the children
can role-play the various creatures.

The children can compose one of the sad
songs that Tselane sang inside the drum.
Have the children use several memories
that she had of happier days and then add a
gentle tune.

What if the "bee plan" had not worked?
Help the class to plan another method of
saving Tselane from the drum.

One day a little girl named Tselane went
down to the river to fetch water. Dip
after dip, she worked to fill her huge
gourd calabash, and as she dipped she sang. The
song was so beautiful that all of the animals
around her, even the crocodile and hippo in the
reeds, all stopped whatever they were doing
and listened to the little girl sing.

In the tall grass, not far from her, a man with
a drum sat and listened too. Now if he had
been a good man, he would have listened quietly
and then gone away. But he was *not* a good
man, but a very bad *zimwe*, and so a bad idea
came into his head. Just as Tselane had almost
filled her calabash with water, the man sneaked
up behind her as she sang and thrust her into
his drum, which was bigger than she was.

Before she could cry out, the man said to her,
"Little girl, you sing well. Now, listen to me.
When I beat this drum, you must sing, as well
and as long as you can. If you do not sing, I
will beat *you* instead of my drum!"

Tselane was frightened, and so she told him
she would do what he said. So the man took his
big drum with the little girl inside and went
away.

When he came to a village some distance
away, it was nearly evening, and he stopped by
the village and asked if he might spend the
night. The chief answered that he could, and so
the man said that he wished to play the drum

for all the people to thank them for their
hospitality.

"Boom! Boom!" He beat the drum and
Tselane began to sing. She sang and sang and
all of the villagers listened happily to the
beautiful music.

When she stopped they all cried out, "Please,
stranger, play your singing drum again!"

But the man answered, "I am hungry and
tired, and I cannot play my drum until I eat."

When the people heard this they hurried to
their gardens and filled their baskets with all
the good things they could find to eat. There
were big golden pumpkins, and fat yams, and
red beans, and bananas. These they cooked and
brought to the man, along with fresh goat's
milk and sweet honey-beer. He ate and ate and
drank and drank until all the good things were
gone. Then—"Boom! Boom!"—he beat the drum
and Tselane began to sing, and she sang and
sang and sang until the moon was high in the
sky. Then she sang lullabies and did not stop
until all of the villagers were nodding their
heads sleepily.

Then, when everyone had gone to bed, the
man opened up the top of the drum and gave
the little girl five small cold beans that were
all that was left of his big dinner, even though
she was quite hungry after so much singing.

When morning came, the man went away,
taking his wonderful drum, and went on to

another village. The same thing happened as the night before, but this time the people even cooked him a chicken stew which he gobbled up, saving none at all for Tselane. From village to village he went, and wherever he went, it was always the same. No one had ever heard such beautiful sounds as came from the singing drum, and so wherever he went people feasted him with all the good things they could find.

But did he share any of this with poor little Tselane, locked in the dark drum? No, he did not; he only gave her enough to keep her voice from growing small and weak . . . four or five cold beans, or a few pumpkin seeds.

When Tselane had not returned to her village her mother and father had gone to the river to look for her. Not a sign of her did they see—except her big calabash, nearly filled with water. Along the river's edge a crocodile blinked at them, and they asked him if he had eaten their little girl, but he shook his head and swam away.

A giraffe was munching at the treetops and they called to him, "O Giraffe . . . you with your long neck that looks over the wide plain . . . have you seen our little girl?"

But the giraffe shook his head and went on eating.

They called to a lion in the grass, "Where is our little girl—Tselane who sings so sweetly? Have you eaten her?"

But the lion shook his mane and ran away.

On and on the mother and father wandered until they met an elephant.

"O Elephant . . . with your great ears . . . have you heard news of our little lost girl?"

But the elephant shook his head sadly, and slowly ambled away.

Then they met a hyena, an ugly, unpleasant fellow.

"Hyena, please, do you know where our little girl—Tselane who sings so sweetly—where she might be?"

But the hyena only laughed a nasty, sneering laugh and slunk away.

For weeks and weeks Tselane's mother and father wandered, always asking for their little girl, but no one had seen or heard of her. They grew dusty and ragged from their journeying from forest to plain, from village to village, but their little girl was not to be found.

One evening, tired and hungry, they stopped at a village and asked to spend the night. The villagers welcomed them and told them that there was another stranger staying in the village that night, but there was still room for more. The other stranger was the man with the drum that sang.

"Boom! Boom!"—he beat the drum and it began to sing.

Tselane, hidden inside, sang songs about the beautiful things she had known when she lived outside the drum in the bright sunshine . . . about little antelopes running through the tall grass . . . about the gentle bleating of newborn baby kids, and about blue mountains reaching for the sky.

Because she was sure she would never see these things again she sang sad songs about happy things, and they were lovelier than any songs she had ever before sung. All the people held their breath so as not to miss a note.

Except one. No sooner had Tselane begun to sing when her mother, sitting close to the drummer, started to cry out for she recognized the voice of her dear little girl. But her father looked sternly at his wife, and so she said nothing, but instead sat very still and listened. For hours and hours the drum sang, and each song was more beautiful than the one before.

When the singing was done—for at last the man said he could play no longer unless he was fed—all of the people brought him the best foods they had, and he ate and ate and ate.

"I am thirsty!" he cried out when he had eaten enough for ten men, and then the people brought him calabashes and ostrich-egg cups of sweet honey-beer, and he drank and drank and drank, while Tselane's father sat near him and flattered him about his wonderful drum and urged him to eat and drink some more.

At last, when he had drunk enough for twenty men, he gave a great yawn, and fell asleep. All the people in the village went to their houses to sleep, but Tselane's parents only pretended to sleep. When they were sure that everyone was asleep and the drummer was snoring louder than a lion, they crept up to him. Quietly, quietly, they untied the thongs that held the drum skin to the drum and peeped inside. There was their little girl, small and thin and frightened and lonely.

"Come out, come out," they whispered to her and held her tight.

Then her father took a little fire on a stick and crept out into the forest.

Near an old tree he held the stick of fire, and after a moment many, many bees came out of a hole in the tree, for they did not like the smoke from the man's fire.

As they swarmed around not knowing where to go, the man put the stick close to them and they flew ahead of him to escape the smoke. In this way he drove them on ahead of him and right back to the village of sleeping people, and up to the man's empty drum.

Seeing the nice hole in the drum, quite like a hole in a dead tree, the bees all flew in, and the father snapped the drum skin over the drum and smiled.

Then the family went to sleep.

Morning came, and when everyone awoke they begged the man to play his drum again. No one noticed the strange little girl who was there, for they talked of nothing but the beautiful songs of the drum.

"Please, please," they begged the man over and over again. "Play the drum for us again before you go."

And the man rubbed his stomach and said, "I could play the drum quite well, if I only had a little breakfast!"

And the people then promised him that they would feast him with even more food than the night before, and would give him many presents besides, if he would only play one little short song before they went into their gardens to pick a feast for him—for there was nothing left in their houses.

And so the man agreed: one little song, that was all.

"Boom! Boom!"—he beat the drum, but nothing happened.

"Boom! Boom! BOOM!"—angrily he beat the drum again.

Nothing happened and a few people began to laugh at him.

"BOOM! BOOM! BOOM! BOOM! BOOM! . . . BOOM! BOOM! BOOM!" Again and again he beat the drum, but nothing happened . . . nothing at all. By now all of the people were laughing and laughing at him. Then he threw his drum on the ground, and kicked it and shouted at it, but still the drum was silent.

At last, he picked up the drum and ran angrily out of the village, shouting to the drum, "I told you I would beat you if you did not sing—and now I *will!*"

So saying, he tore off the drum skin to beat Tselane, but—Oh my!

Out came the bees . . . so many of them! "Bzzzzzzzzzzzzzzzzz . . . zzzzzzzzz . . ." and they flew after that man and chased him away, and no one ever saw or heard of him again.

As for Tselane, she sang a beautiful happy song for the people before they went back to their gardens to work, and so everyone gave her good things to eat (for she was very hungry after being in the drum so long), and a pretty necklace besides. Then she and her mother and father began their journey home.

Let's Send a Rocket

After hearing the poem, the children can
join in a chant, calling out the numbers ten
to zero. Then they can all shout out, "Blast
off!"

Ten, nine, eight . . .
Seven, six, five . . .

We'll send up a rocket,
And it will be *live*.

Five, four, three . . .
It's ready to zoom!

We're counting each second,
And soon it will boom!

Get ready for . . . two;
Get ready to go . . .

It's *two*—and it's—one—
We're OFF! It's ZERO!

KIT PATRICKSON

How the Rooster Saved the Day

BY ARNOLD LOBEL

Before the story

Conduct a survey of how the children are awakened on school days. Some ideas to consider are: the time they awake; how they are awakened (e.g. an alarm clock, a parent, the sun); how late they sleep in; how late they stay up; how they finally fall asleep (e.g. counting sheep).

Ask, "How do animals know when to wake up?"

After the story

Building the pattern on the cause and effect relationship in the story, have the class make up other excuses for the Rooster not crowing; e.g. "I've been flying through the forest at night and hooting and hooting."

Discuss with the children how life would be different if the robber had stolen the rooster and the sun had never risen.

Once, long ago, there lived a large and handsome rooster. At the start of each day he would crow to bring up the morning sun.

One dark night a robber crept into the barn where the rooster was sleeping. The robber grabbed the rooster by the throat and said, "Rooster, you will never bring up the morning sun again. I am going to kill you. The world will always be in blackest night. No one will ever see me as I run about the countryside, robbing and plundering."

The rooster, who was brave and clever, put his ear near to the robber's mouth. "What are you saying?" asked the rooster. "I have been swimming around in the pond and quacking and quacking for so long, that I have made myself as deaf as a stone."

When the robber heard this, he threw back his head and laughed. "You cannot quack," said the robber. "It is the ducks who are the quacking ones!"

"Forgive me," said the rooster, "but I have been chasing the cat and barking and barking for so long that my hearing is very bad." At this the robber laughed even more.

"You never bark," he said. "It is the dogs who are the barking ones!"

"I beg your pardon," said the rooster, "but I have been sitting in the mud and oinking and oinking for so long that my poor ears do not work at all."

"Oh, no," said the robber, who was laughing so hard that tears were running down his cheeks. "You do not oink," he said. "It is the pigs who are the oinking ones!"

"I am so sorry," said the rooster, "but I have been chewing the grass in the meadow and mooing and mooing for so long that I do not seem to hear anything."

The robber fell onto the floor in a fit of laughter. "You foolish bird," he cried. "You cannot moo! It is the cows who are the mooing ones!" "Enough of this nonsense!" said the robber. "You are a rooster and roosters are the ones who cock-a-doodle-doo!"

"Pardon my old deaf ears," said the rooster. "I did not hear you. Speak a bit louder if you will."

"Cock-a-doodle-doo!" said the robber.

"Please speak up," said the rooster, "for I am so very deaf."

"COCK-A-DOODLE-DOO!" shouted the robber as loudly as he could.

The darkness of night faded and the great yellow sun came up over the eastern hills.

"You have crowed the sun up for me and I thank you," said the rooster. "I have heard you clearly, for my ears are as sharp as the point of my beak."

The robber, who was well known about the land, was much afraid to be seen by the light of day. He jumped out of the barn and ran away over the fields.

The robber ran far, far away and the rooster still crows to bring up the morning sun.

What's in There?

This old rhyme can be read to the children.
On the second reading they can join in by
asking the questions, and the teacher can
give the responses.

What's in there?
Gold and money.
Where's my share of it?
The mousie ran away with it.
Where's the mousie?
In her housie.
Where's her housie?
In the wood.
Where's the wood?
The fire burnt it.
Where's the fire?
The water quenched it.
Where's the water?
The brown bull drank it.
Where's the brown bull?
Back of the hill.
Where's the hill?
All clad with snow.
Where's the snow?
The sun melted it.
Where's the sun?
High, high up in the air!

TRADITIONAL

Why Mosquitoes Buzz in People's Ears

RETOLD BY VERNA AARDEMA

Before the story

Play the game "Gossip" with the children. Whisper a funny statement into one child's ear and have that child whisper it to the next, and so on around the circle. The last child repeats the statement aloud, and the children can compare it with the original. Then discuss the importance of giving messages clearly and listening carefully to what was said.

After the story

Create a *pourquoi* story about "How the Zebra Got Its Stripes" or "How the Wolf Got Its Howl" with the class. If possible, help the children to use the cumulative pattern as established in "Why Mosquitoes Buzz in People's Ears."

One morning a mosquito saw an iguana drinking at a waterhole. The mosquito said, "Iguana, you will never believe what I saw yesterday."

"Try me," said the iguana.

The mosquito said, "I saw a farmer digging yams that were almost as big as I am."

"What's a mosquito compared to a yam?" snapped the iguana grumpily. "I would rather be deaf than listen to such nonsense!" Then he stuck two sticks in his ears and went off, *mek, mek, mek, mek*, through the reeds.

The iguana was still grumbling to himself when he happened to pass by a python.

The big snake raised his head and said, "Good morning, Iguana."

The iguana did not answer but lumbered on, bobbing his head, *badamin, badamin*.

"Now, why won't he speak to me?" said the python to himself. "Iguana must be angry about something. I'm afraid he is plotting some mischief against me!" He began looking for somewhere to hide. The first likely place he found was a rabbit hole, and in it he went, *wasawusu, wasawusu, wasawusu*.

When the rabbit saw the big snake coming into her burrow, she was terrified. She scurried out through her back way and bounded, *krik, krik, krik*, across a clearing.

A crow saw the rabbit running for her life. He flew into the forest crying *kaa, kaa, kaa*! It was his duty to spread the alarm in case of danger.

A monkey heard the crow. He was sure that some dangerous beast was prowling near. He began screeching and leaping *kili wili* through the trees to help warn the other animals.

As the monkey was crashing through the treetops, he happened to land on a dead limb. It broke and fell on an owl's nest, killing one of the owlets.

Mother Owl was not at home. For though she usually hunted only in the night, this morning she was still out searching for one more tidbit to satisfy her hungry babies. When she returned to the nest, she found one of them dead. Her other children told her that the monkey had killed it. All that day and all that night, she sat in her tree—so sad, so sad, so sad!

Now it was Mother Owl who woke the sun each day so that the dawn could come. But this time, when she should have hooted for the sun, she did not do it.

The night grew longer and longer. The animals of the forest knew it was lasting much too long. The feared that the sun would never come back.

At last King Lion called a meeting of the animals. They came and sat down, *pem, pem, pem*, around a council fire. Mother Owl did not come, so the antelope was sent to fetch her.

When she arrived, King Lion asked, "Mother Owl, why have you not called the sun? The night has lasted long, long, long, and everyone is worried.

Mother Owl said, "Monkey killed one of my

owlets. Because of that, I cannot bear to wake the sun."

The king said to the gathered animals: "Did you hear? It was the monkey who killed the owlet—and now Mother Owl won't wake the sun so that the day can come."

Then King Lion called the monkey. He came before him nervously glancing from side to side, *rim, rim, rim, rim*.

"Monkey," said the king, "why did you kill one of Mother Owl's babies?"

"Oh, King," said the monkey, "it was the crow's fault. He was calling and calling to warn us of danger. And I went leaping through the trees to help. A limb broke under me, and it fell *taaa* on the owl's nest."

The king said to the council: "So, it was the crow who alarmed the monkey, who killed the owlet—and now Mother Owl won't wake the sun so that the day can come."

Then the king called for the crow. That big bird came flapping up. He said, "King Lion, it was the rabbit's fault! I saw her running for her life in the daytime. Wasn't that reason enough to spread an alarm?"

The king nodded his head and said to the council: "So, it was the rabbit who startled the crow, who alarmed the monkey, who killed the owlet—and now Mother Owl won't wake the sun so that the day can come."

Then King Lion called the rabbit. The timid little creature stood before him, one trembling paw drawn up uncertainly.

"Rabbit," cried the king, "why did you break a law of nature and go running, running, running, in the daytime?"

"Oh, King," said the rabbit, "it was the python's fault. I was in my house minding my own business when that big snake came in and chased me out."

The king said to the council:
"So, it was the python
who scared the rabbit,
who startled the crow,
who alarmed the monkey,
who killed the owlet—
and now Mother Owl won't wake the sun
so that the day can come."

King Lion called the python, who came slithering, *wasawusu, wasawusu*, past the other animals. "But, King," he cried, "it was the iguana's fault! He wouldn't speak to me. And I thought he was plotting some mischief against me. When I crawled into the rabbit's hole, I was only trying to hide."

The king said to the council:
"So, it was the iguana
who frightened the python,
who scared the rabbit,
who startled the crow,
who alarmed the monkey,
who killed the owlet—
and now Mother Owl won't wake the sun
so that the day can come."

Now the iguana was not at the meeting. For he had not heard the summons.

The antelope was sent to fetch him.

All the animals laughed when they saw the iguana coming, *badamin, badamin*, with the sticks still stuck in his ears!

King Lion pulled out the sticks, *purup, purup*. Then he asked, "Iguana, what evil have you been plotting against the python?"

"None! None at all!" cried the iguana. "Python is my friend!"

"Then why wouldn't you say good morning to me?" demanded the snake.

"I didn't hear you, or even see you!" said the iguana. "Mosquito told me such a big lie, I couldn't bear to listen to it. So I put sticks in my ears!"

"*Nge, nge, nge*," laughed the lion. "So that's why you had sticks in your ears!"

"Yes," said the iguana. "It was the mosquito's fault."

King Lion said to the council:
"So, it was the mosquito
who annoyed the iguana,
who frightened the python,
who scared the rabbit,
who startled the crow,
who alarmed the monkey,
who killed the owlet—
and now Mother Owl won't wake the sun
so that the day can come."

"Punish the mosquito! Punish the mosquito!" cried all the animals.

When Mother Owl heard that, she was satisfied. She turned her head toward the east and hooted: "*Hoo! Hooooo! Hooooooo!*"

And the sun came up.

Meanwhile the mosquito had listened to it all from a nearby bush. She crept under a curly leaf, *semm*, and was never found and brought before the council.

But because of this the mosquito has a guilty conscience. To this day she goes about whining in people's ears: "Zeee! Is everyone still angry at me?"

When she does that, she gets an honest answer.

Ferry Boats

Read the poem aloud to the children. Ask
them what boats they have seen or taken a
ride on. How many types of boats can they
brainstorm? (e.g. sailboat, Noah's ark,
submarine)

Over the river,
Over the bay,
Ferry-boats travel
Every day.

Most of the people
Crowd to the side
Just to enjoy
Their ferry-boat ride.

Watching the seagulls,
Laughing with friends,
I'm always sorry
When the ride ends.

JAMES S. TIPPETT

Apt. 3

By Ezra Jack Keats

Before the story

Lead a discussion about apartments—those
the children live in, those they have visited,
and those they have seen on television.
Questions you could ask are: "What is it like
living in an apartment? Do you know your
neighbours? How would you know if someone
is home without knocking on the door?
How do children visit an apartment on
Hallowe'en? How do things get delivered?
Who lets people in at the front door of the
building? Who shovels the sidewalk?"

After the story

Ask the children, "How could Sam and Ben
help their new neighbour in the future?
How could he be their friend?"

Create a "sound environment" for the
children to identify as they close their eyes,
e.g. munch a potato chip, crinkle tinfoil,
run a toy car on a table, click a ballpoint
pen, wave a cloth, close a book.

The rain fell steadily. It beat against the
windows, softening the sounds of the
city. As Sam gazed out, he heard
someone in the building playing a harmonica. It
filled him with sad and lonely feelings—like
the rain outside. He had heard that music
before. Each time it was different. "Who's that
playing?" Sam wondered.

Sam went into the hall and listened. No
music. His little brother Ben tagged along. Sam
listened at the door across the hall. Crunch,
crunch, crunch. Crunch, crackle, crunch!
Someone—or something—turned the knob.

Out came Mr. Muntz, crunching a mouthful
of potato chips.

They waited until he was gone. There was
one door left on their floor. Through it came
smells of cigarettes and cooking. A family was
arguing. But no music.

They walked down to the floor below. In Apt.
9 a dog was barking. Next door a mother sang
softly to her crying baby. At Apt. 7, not a
sound.

The hall light was broken. At Apt. 6, there
was a ball game on TV. It sounded like a million
people were in there cheering. Apt. 5—loud,
juicy snoring.

Ben bumped into an old, worn-out mattress.

"That snorer sure's enjoying his new one,"
Sam said.

Apt. 4—more yelling.

Finally, the ground floor. The door of Apt. 1
opened.

"The caretaker!" Sam whispered.

They hid under the stairs. The caretaker
grumbled to himself as he left the building and
slammed the door.

"That guy hates everyone," said Ben.

Apt. 3 was quiet. Just a container of milk
outside the door. They stopped in front of Apt.
2—Betsy's door.

Sam thought, "Maybe she'll come out and I'll
say hello to her." He decided to hang around.

"Let's rest a little," he said. They sat on the
steps.

But no Betsy. And no music.

"C'mon, let's go home," said Ben.

As they turned to go upstairs, Sam noticed
that the container of milk was gone!

He went over to take a good look. The door
was open a little. He peeked in.

"WELL?" A sharp voice startled Sam.

"We didn't take the milk!" he blurted.

But the man was shouting, "O.K., nosy! Have
a good look!"

Sam could make out a figure at a table. It
was the blind man's apartment!

"Come on in, you two! What's the matter—
scared?"

They were so scared they went in. "There's
the milk," Sam shouted. "We didn't take it!"

"Who said you did?" snapped the man. "I

brought it in myself. Stop shaking, kids. Shut the door and sit down."

Sam shut the door and sat down.

"How'd you know we're kids?" asked Ben.

"I know about boys. You live upstairs," said the man. "I know something else about you, Sam."

"What?" whispered Sam.

"You like the little girl across the hall. The way you slow down when you pass her door. The real nice way you say 'Hi, Betsy,' and she says 'Hi, Sam.' "

Ben giggled.

Sam jumped up. "Who's nosy now?" he yelled. "I know about you too. You sit around here, finding out other people's secrets!"

The man's face took on a faraway look. "I know plenty, young fellow. I know when it rains, when it snows, what people are cooking, and what they think they're fighting about.

Secrets? You want to hear some secrets? Listen." He stood up suddenly, raised his harmonica to his mouth, and began to play. He played purples and greys and rain and smoke and the sounds of night.

Sam sat quietly and listened. He felt that all the sights and sounds and colours from outside had come into the room and were floating around. He floated with them.

Ben's eyes were closed, and he was smiling.

After a while, Sam turned to the man and said, "Would you like to take a walk with us tomorrow?"

The music became so soft and quiet they could barely hear it.

Then the dark room filled with wild, happy music. It bounced from wall to wall.

Sam and Ben looked at each other. They couldn't wait for tomorrow.

My Big Blue Boat

Read aloud or sing the poem to the children
and have them join in and mime the motions
of the row boat by facing a partner, joining
hands, and pulling backwards and forwards
as they sing.

I love to row in my big blue boat,
My big blue boat, my big blue boat;
I love to row in my big blue boat,
Out on the deep blue sea.

My big blue boat has two red sails,
Two red sails, two red sails;
My big blue boat has two red sails,
Two red sails.

So come for a row in my big blue boat,
My big blue boat, my big blue boat;
So come for a row in my big blue boat,
Out on the deep blue sea.

TRADITIONAL

Mud Puddle

By Robert N. Munsch

Before the story

Discuss the occasions when it is permissable to get dirty, e.g. helping in the garden, playing in the sandbox.

Ask the children why it is so difficult for them to keep clean for their parents and teachers. Why do adults like children to be clean and tidy?

After the story

Conduct a storytelling session by having the children describe the mud puddle and an adventure that they have had with it, either imagined or from the story.

Ask how they would create the biggest mud puddle in the world.

Jule Ann's mother bought her clean new clothes.

Jule Ann put on a clean new shirt, clean pants, and went out to play under the apple tree in the back yard.

Unfortunately, there was a mud puddle hiding up in the apple tree.

It saw Jule Ann and jumped right on her head.

She got completely all over muddy.

Even her ears were full of mud.

Jule Ann ran inside yelling, "Mummy, Mummy! A Mud Puddle jumped on me."

Her mother took off all Jule Ann's clothes and dropped her into a big bathtub. She scrubbed Jule Ann till she was red all over.

Jule Ann put on a clean new shirt, clean new pants and looked carefully out the door.

There was no mud puddle anywhere, so Jule Ann went to play in the sand box next to the house.

Unfortunately, there was a mud puddle hiding on the roof.

It jumped right on Jule Ann's head and she got completely all over muddy. Even her mouth was full of mud.

Jule Ann ran inside yelling, "Mummy, Mummy! A Mud Puddle jumped on me."

Jule Ann's mother took off all Jule Ann's clothes and dropped Jule Ann into a big bathtub full of water. She scrubbed Jule Ann till she was red all over.

Jule Ann put on a clean new shirt, clean new pants and then she put on a big yellow raincoat with a hood. She marched out to the middle of the yard and yelled, "Hey, Mud Puddle!"

Nothing happened. Jule Ann started to get hot, so she slowly pulled back her hood.

Nothing happened, so she slowly took off her raincoat.

As soon as her coat was off the mud puddle ran from behind the dog house and jumped right on Jule Ann's head. She got completely all over muddy. Even her nose was full of mud.

Jule Ann ran inside yelling, "Mummy, Mummy! A Mud Puddle jumped on me."

Jule Ann's mother took off all Jule Ann's clothes and dropped her into a big bathtub full of water. She scrubbed Jule Ann till she was red all over.

Jule Ann put on a clean new shirt, new pants and then she sat beside the door, for she was afraid to go outside.

Suddenly she had an idea!

She got two huge bars of smelly orange soap and hid them in her pockets.

Then she ran to the middle of the yard and yelled, "Hey, Mud Puddle!"

The mud puddle jumped over the fence and ran right toward her.

Jule Ann threw a bar of soap right into the mud puddle's middle.

The mud puddle stopped.

Jule Ann threw the other bar of soap into the mud puddle.

The mud puddle said, "Awk, Yuck, Wackh!" It jumped over the fence and never came back.

I Went to the River

This folk rhyme lets the children join in
immediately, as the teacher can read the
poem aloud and stop before the rhyme word
to allow the children to fill it in. For
example:

> "The bull wouldn't holler,
> So I traded for a _____"

The children can clap along to maintain the
rhythm.

I went to the river
And couldn't get across,
Paid five dollars
For an old gray hoss.

The horse wouldn't pull,
So I traded for a bull;

The bull wouldn't holler,
So I traded for a dollar;

The dollar wouldn't pass,
So I threw it in the grass;

The grass wouldn't grow,
So I traded for a hoe;

The hoe wouldn't dig,
So I traded for a pig;

The pig wouldn't squeal,
So I traded for a wheel;

The wheel wouldn't run,
So I traded for a gun;

The gun wouldn't shoot,
So I traded for a boot;

The boot wouldn't fit,
So I thought I'd better quit.

TRADITIONAL

I'm Tipingee, She's Tipingee, We're Tipingee, Too

RETOLD BY DIANE WOLKSTEIN

Before the story

Ask, "Do you know anyone who has the same name as you? How can people tell you apart? What if all the girls had one name and all the boys had one name? Do you know any stories about people with strange names?" (e.g. Rumpelstiltskin)

After the story

Present the children with this "what if" situation: The man took Tipingee away to be his servant. How would her friends rescue her now?

There was once a girl named Tipingee who lived with her stepmother. Her father was dead. The stepmother was selfish, and even though she lived in the girl's house, she did not like to share what she earned with the girl.

One morning, the stepmother was cooking sweets to sell in the market. The fire under her pot went out. Tipingee was in school, so the stepmother had to go herself into the forest to find more firewood. She walked for a long time, but she did not find any wood. She continued walking. Then she came to a place where there was firewood everywhere. She gathered it into a bundle. But it was too heavy to lift up onto her head. Still, she did not want anyone else to have any of the firewood. So standing in the middle of the forest she cried out: "My friends, there is so much wood here and at home I have no wood. Where can I find a person who will help me carry the firewood?"

Suddenly an old man appeared. "I will help you to carry the firewood. But then what will you give me?"

"I have very little," the woman said, "but I will find something to give you when we get to my house."

The old man carried the firewood for the stepmother, and when they got to the house he said, "I have carried the firewood for you. Now what will you give me?"

"I will give you a servant girl. I will give you my stepdaughter, Tipingee."

Now Tipingee was in the house, and when she heard her name she ran to the door and listened.

"Tomorrow I will send my stepdaughter to the well at noon for water. She will be wearing a red dress, call her by her name, Tipingee, and she will come to you. Then you can take her."

"Very well," said the man, and he went away.

Tipingee ran to her friends. She ran to the houses of all the girls in her class and asked them to wear red dresses the next day.

At noon the next day the old man went to the well. He saw one little girl dressed in red. He saw a second little girl dressed in red. He saw a third girl in red.

"Which of you is Tipingee?" he asked.

The first little girl said: "I'm Tipingee."

The second little girl said: "She's Tipingee."

The third little girl said: "We're Tipingee, too."

"Which of you is Tipingee?" asked the old man.

Then the little girls began to clap and jump up and down and chant:

> I'm Tipingee,
> She's Tipingee,
> We're Tipingee, too.
>
> I'm Tipingee,
> She's Tipingee,
> We're Tipingee, too.

Rah! The old man went to the woman and said, "You tricked me. All the girls were dressed in red and each one said she was Tipingee."

"That is impossible," said the stepmother. "Tomorrow she will wear a black dress. Then you will find her. The one wearing a black dress will be Tipingee. Call her and take her."

But Tipingee heard what her stepmother said and ran and begged all her friends to wear black dresses the next day.

When the old man went to the well the next day, he saw one little girl dressed in black. He saw a second little girl dressed in black. He saw a third girl in black.

"Which of you is Tipingee?" he asked.

The first little girl said: "I'm Tipingee."

The second little girl said: "She's Tipingee."

The third little girl said: "We're Tipingee, too."

"Which of you is Tipingee?" asked the old man.

And the girls joined hands and skipped about and sang:

> I'm Tipingee,
> She's Tipingee,
> We're Tipingee, too.
>
> I'm Tipingee,
> She's Tipingee,
> We're Tipingee, too.

The man was getting angry. He went to the stepmother and said, "You promised to pay me and you are only giving me problems. You tell me Tipingee and everyone here is Tipingee, Tipingee, Tipingee, Tipingee. If this happens a third time, I will come and take you for my servant."

"My dear sir," said the stepmother, "tomorrow she will be in red, completely in red, call her and take her."

And again Tipingee ran and told her friends to dress in red.

At noon the next day, the old man arrived at the well. He saw one little girl dressed in red. He saw a second little girl dressed in red. He saw a third girl in red.

"Which of you is Tipingee?" he asked.

"I'm Tipingee," said the first girl.

"She's Tipingee," said the second girl.

"We're Tipingee, too," said the third girl.

"WHICH OF YOU IS TIPINGEE?" the old man shouted. But the girls just clapped and jumped up and down and sang:

> I'm Tipingee,
> She's Tipingee,
> We're Tipingee, too.
>
> I'm Tipingee,
> She's Tipingee,
> We're Tipingee, too.

The old man knew he would never find Tipingee. He went to the stepmother and took her away. When Tipingee returned home, she was gone. So she lived in her own house with all her father's belongings, and she was happy.